TABLE OF CONTENTS

At MegaGeex, we love making content designed to help build better learners. Our resources empower parents and educators alike to give kids hands-on inspiration to grow into the world-changing adults we want them to be. To be able to do that, we need your help to guarantee that we have the resources to continue to create great content.

If our resources are used beyond home and personal use, in a classroom, or other educational settings where you receive compensation, then a professional license is required.

Each professional license allows for a single teacher to use the resource for students in the teacher's class or block of classes. Price is determined by the number of students using the resource. If more than one teacher in your school wants access to the materials, then additional licenses are available for purchase.

Questions? Feel free to reach out to us at hello@megageex.com and we'll be happy to help. If someone you know would like to use one of our printable pages, have them check out www.megageex.com for our full catalog.

Hello!

If we could look back over 600 years, most would be amazed at the developments, discoveries, and inventions that have changed the world. Human-kind, in this small space of time, has made advancements in every area of our lives. Communication is possible with people thousands of miles away- in real time! Circling the planet is accomplished in only days. Television, movies, computers, automobiles, only begin to tell the story of the mind-blowing improvements that benefit us all.

These awesome accomplishments were made possible by regular people who had extraordinary qualities. Men and women who shared two common traits: Passion and Grit. In the face of challenges and even failures, they never quit, and they succeeded in what many viewed as impossible.

With dedication and persistence, they overcame whatever hurdles given to them by society during their lives. Women such as Ada Lovelace, Marie Curie, and Jane Austen pursued their education despite laws and views that said they could not. George Washington Carver never gave up in the face of racial discrimination. And Albert Einstein could not find a job as a professor but he still continued work on his theories. These are just a few examples of the character of these remarkable individuals.

In 2018, Daniel Scalosub, embarked on a mission of his own. He wanted his twin daughters to know that they can do ANYTHING. And what better way to prove this to them than to share the incredible stories of these inventors, writers, scientists and artists, and entrepreneurs. Daniel founded Megageex to bring knowledge, and more importantly, inspiration and encouragement to kids everywhere.

Feel free to explore our unique products. Each one is designed with the sole purpose to inspire and teach through play and creativity.

Connect your kids with the world's greatest minds and get ready for a learning journey like no other.

Welcome to Megageex!

Welcome to the MegaGeex Complete Division Playbook part1!
We are excited for you to practice division in a new and fun way.

On your mark! Get set! Go learn!!

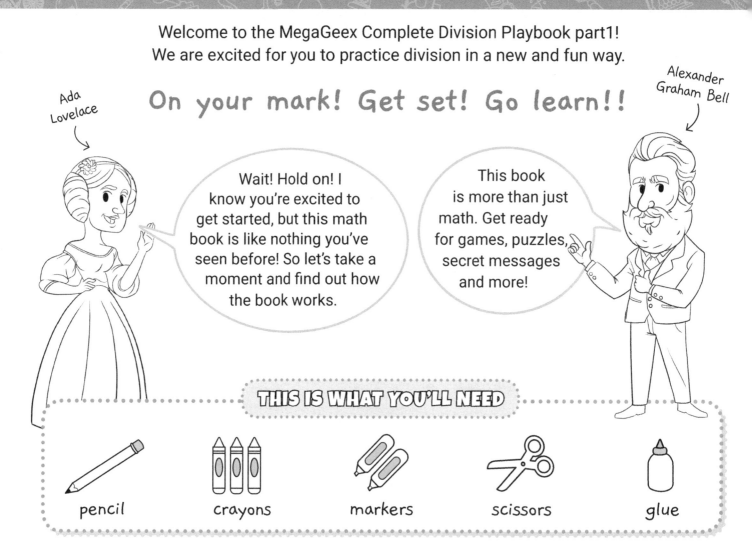

Ada Lovelace

Wait! Hold on! I know you're excited to get started, but this math book is like nothing you've seen before! So let's take a moment and find out how the book works.

Alexander Graham Bell

This book is more than just math. Get ready for games, puzzles, secret messages and more!

THIS IS WHAT YOU'LL NEED

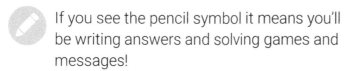

pencil   crayons   markers   scissors   glue

Be on the lookout for symbols like these:

If you see the pencil symbol it means you'll be writing answers and solving games and messages!

See the scissors? This means you'll be snipping away at puzzle pieces.

The light bulb symbol means you need to turn on the lights! No actually, this symbol means there is a cool fact about the Megageex or math that you'll be learning.

The question mark lets you know there is a cool trivia question to answer about the Megageex. Once you learn some of the answers, quiz your parents with the questions! They'll be impressed with how big your brain is getting.

Isaac Newton

If you are already the "Supreme Grand Master" of the times tables that is awesome! But, if you need some help, we've included a times table chart to use if you get stuck on any problem.

The Wright Brothers

If you're a division newbie or think that some review might help before you start the book, check out the teaching pages. You'll see great examples and explanations of how division works!

Jane Austin

Don't have a cow! The division problems may look different than what you see in your school books depending on what country you live in (you can find more information on the different ways to write division problems on page 14).

Charles Darwin

In this book, the division problems are written like this:

$$8 \div 2 = 4$$

We would love to hear from you and see your work as you complete the book. Let us know how you like it and share your favorite activity with us:
hello@megageex.com

You know what? YOU ARE READY!

Now...go play, learn, and grow!

Nikola Tesla

Serbian scientist, inventor, and futurist (1856 - 1942). Designed the alternating current (AC) model that provides electricity to homes. Pioneered radio transmissions and wireless technology.

Rosalind Franklin

English chemist (1920 - 1958). Proved the double-helix model of DNA, the building blocks of all life. Her work on the structure of viruses contributed to founding the field of structural virology.

Thomas Edison

American inventor and entrepreneur (1847 - 1931). Considered "America's greatest inventor". Invented the light bulb, the phonograph, the first motion picture camera, early electric power generators, and over a thousand other inventions.

George Washington Carver

American agricultural chemist and agronomist (1860s - 1942). Developed methods for improving soil fertility, and crops versatility. Created products with peanuts, which gave him the nickname "the Peanut Man".

Galileo Galilei

Italian scientist (1564 - 1642). Considered the "father of modern physics". Pioneered the "scientific method" of learning through observation, asking questions and seeking answers by doing experiments.

The Wright Brothers

American aviation pioneers and inventors (Orville 1871 - 1948, Wilbur 1867 - 1912). They invented and built the first motorized airplane and were the first men to fly it in December 1903.

Isaac Newton

English mathematician and scientist (1642 - 1727). Formulated the laws of gravity, motion, and energy. Developed calculus, a new type of math for understanding and describing continuous change.

Madam CJ Walker

American businesswoman, entrepreneur, and social activist (1867 - 1919). Created the first cosmetics and hair care line of products for African-American women. First self-made American female millionaire.

Wolfgang Amadeus Mozart

Austrian composer and child prodigy (1756 - 1791). Considered one of the most popular composers in western history, having composed more than 600 works. His music had a tremendous influence on subsequent western music.

Alexander Graham Bell

Scottish scientist, inventor, and teacher of the deaf (1847 - 1922). Invented the first practical telephone and founded AT&T, the world's first telephone company.

Jane Austen

English writer and author (1775 - 1817) who wrote such classic books as *Pride & Prejudice*, *Emma*, and *Sense & Sensibility* which challenged country life in 1800s century England.

Charles Darwin

English naturalist and biologist (1809 - 1882). Pioneered the science of evolution. His work *On the Origin of Species* shows how beings evolve over time through natural selection.

Ada Lovelace

English mathematician and writer (1815 - 1852). Regarded as the "world's first computer programmer". Wrote the first computer algorithm based on Charles Babbage's Analytical Machine.

Leonardo Da Vinci

Italian inventor, artist, and naturalist (1452 - 1519) whose wide-ranging works include the Mona Lisa, the first helicopter, and is considered one of the most brilliant people to have ever lived.

Alan Turing

English mathematician (1912 - 1954). Considered the "father of computer science" and pioneered artificial intelligence. Built early computers to break German codes and help win World War II.

Marie Curie

Polish physicist and chemist (1867 - 1934). The first woman to win the Nobel Prize for her discovery of radioactivity, and the first person to win the Nobel twice. Discovered the elements radium and polonium.

Albert Einstein

German physicist (1879 - 1955). One of the world's most influential scientists, whose work on light, gravity, time and space changed the way we understand our universe. Formulated the Theory of Relativity and Nobel Prize winner in Physics.

Madam
C. J. Walker

You're probably excited to get started, but let's review multiplication facts first! Fill in the chart below.

X	1	2	3	4	5	6	7	8	9	10	11	12
1	1	2	3	4	5	6	7	8	9	10	11	12
2	2	4	6	8	10	12	14	16	18	20	22	24
3	3	6	9	12	15	18	21	24	27	30	33	36
4	4	8	12	16	20	24	28	32	36	40	44	48
5	5	10	15	20	25	30	35	40	45	50	55	60
6	6	12	18	24	30	36	42	48	54	60	66	72
7	7	14	21	28	35	42	49	56	63	70	77	84
8	8	16	24	32	40	48	56	64	72	80	88	96
9	9	18	27	36	45	54	63	72	81	90	99	108
10	10	20	30	40	50	60	70	80	90	100	110	120
11	11	22	33	44	55	66	77	88	99	110	111	122
12	12	24	36	48	60	72	84	96	108	120	132	144

As you're working through the book, you might get stuck! Keep this chart to use if you need some help.

Madam C. J. Walker

X	1	2	3	4	5	6	7	8	9	10	11	12
1	1	2	3	4	5	6	7	8	9	10	11	12
2	2	4	6	8	10	12	14	16	18	20	22	24
3	3	6	9	12	15	18	21	24	27	30	33	36
4	4	8	12	16	20	24	28	32	36	40	44	48
5	5	10	15	20	25	30	35	40	45	50	55	60
6	6	12	18	24	30	36	42	48	54	60	66	72
7	7	14	21	28	35	42	49	56	63	70	77	84
8	8	16	24	32	40	48	56	64	72	80	88	96
9	9	18	27	36	45	54	63	72	81	90	99	108
10	10	20	30	40	50	60	70	80	90	100	110	120
11	11	22	33	44	55	66	77	88	99	110	121	132
12	12	24	36	48	60	72	84	96	108	120	132	144

Division is the breaking up of a number into an equal number of parts.

For example: *Each one of my baskets needs the same number of apples. How many apples will go in each basket?*

Isaac Newton

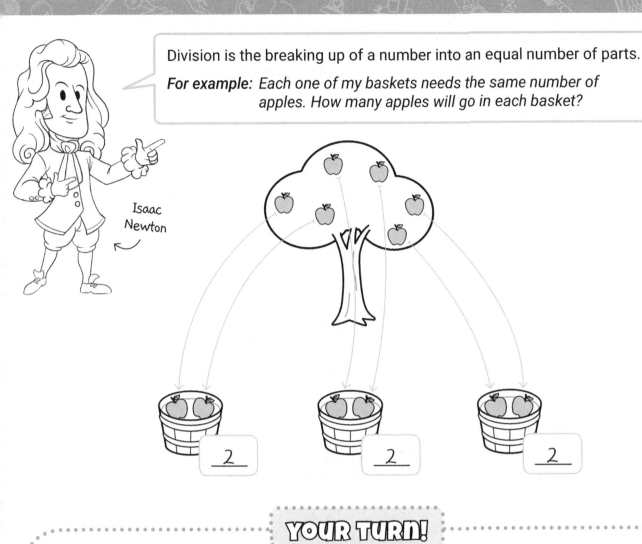

<u>2</u>   <u>2</u>   <u>2</u>

YOUR TURN!

Now Isaac needs to fill 3 baskets with the same number of apples. There are 9 apples on the tree. Draw the number of apples will go in each basket?

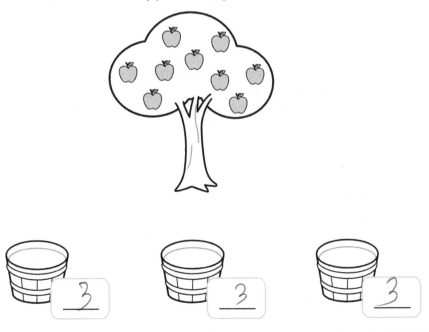

<u>3</u>   <u>3</u>   <u>3</u>

Division is the inverse operation, or the "opposite" of multiplication. When **multiplying** equal groups are joined together.

George Whashington Carver

3 x 2 = 6

When **dividing**, a number is broken up into equal parts. Let's begin with 6 peanuts that will be broken up into 3 equal parts or groups.

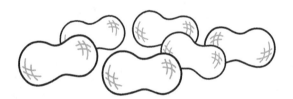

If 6 peanuts are divided into 3 groups, there are 2 peanuts in each group. The division problem would look like this.

6 ÷ 3 = 2

In a division problem there is a **dividend**, **divisor**, and **quotient**.

Dividend: this is the number that is going to be broken up or divided.

Divisor: this is the number we divide by or the number of times we are "breaking up" the dividend (see above)

Quotient: the answer or result we get when we divide a number(dividend) by the divisor.

Galileo Galilei

Division problems can be written in different ways too.

 *Isaac Newton*

 *Leonardo Da Vinci*

Marie Curie

If 12 (dividend) apples are divided between 2 (divisor) people, then each person gets 6 apples (Quotient).

If Leonardo has 8 (dividend) paint brushes, and he has 4 (divisor) art students, then each student gets 2 (quotient) brushes.

Marie Curie has 4 (dividend) beakers. She wants the same number of beakers on 2 (divisor) tables. Each table will have 2 (quotient) beakers.

6 Quotient

Divisor 2 | 12 Dividend

Dividend **8**
—————— = **2** Quotient
Divisor **4**

Dividend
4 ÷ 2 = 2 Quotient
Divisor

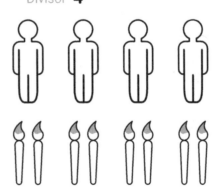

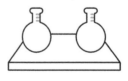

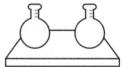

Now that we understand division and each of its parts, let's dive into the games!

15

Matching Game. Match the division problem on the left side of the page to its answer on the right side.

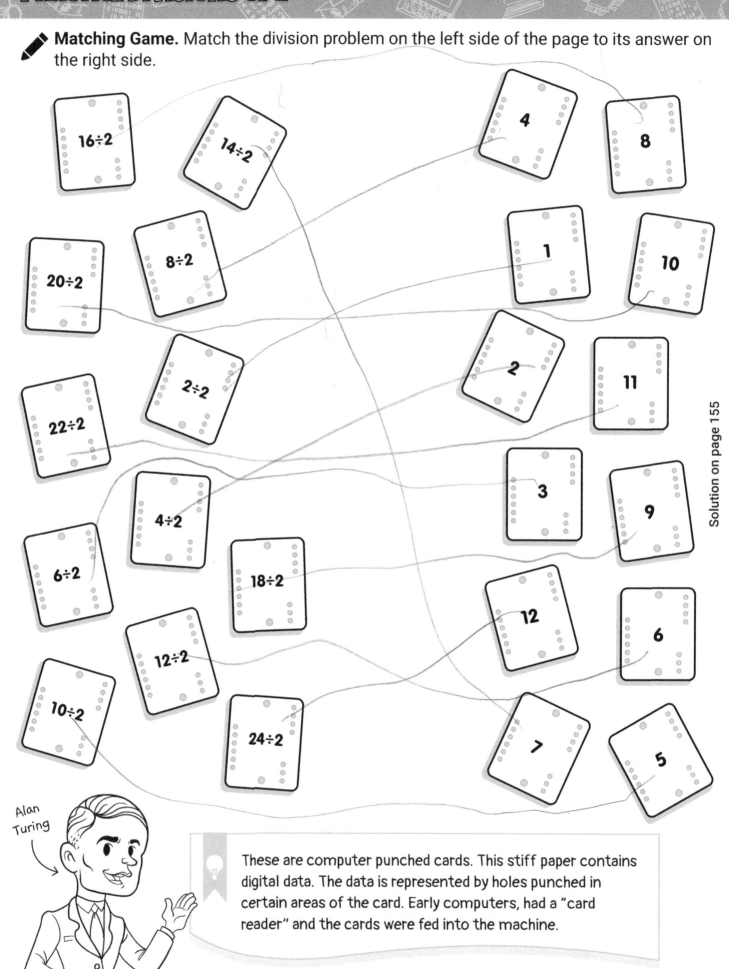

Solution on page 155

16÷2 14÷2 20÷2 8÷2 22÷2 2÷2 4÷2 6÷2 18÷2 12÷2 10÷2 24÷2

4 8 1 10 2 11 3 9 12 6 7 5

Alan Turing

These are computer punched cards. This stiff paper contains digital data. The data is represented by holes punched in certain areas of the card. Early computers, had a "card reader" and the cards were fed into the machine.

✏️ Complete the dot-to-dot by finding the quotients. Start with the division problem that has an answer of 1.

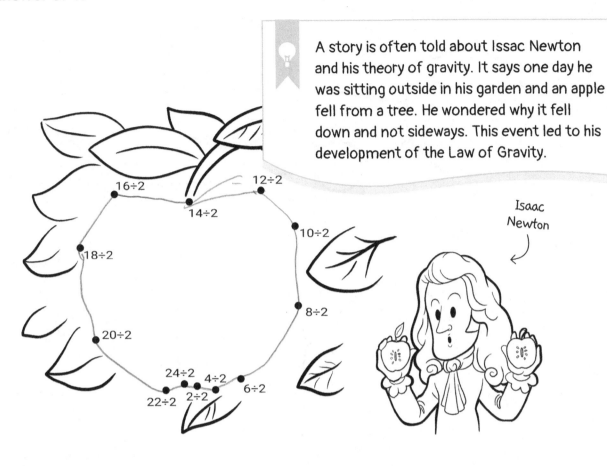

A story is often told about Issac Newton and his theory of gravity. It says one day he was sitting outside in his garden and an apple fell from a tree. He wondered why it fell down and not sideways. This event led to his development of the Law of Gravity.

Isaac Newton

Solution on page 155

✏️ Find the answers to each division problem. Write the word(s) on the lines with the matching answers to see the message.

<u>If i have</u>   <u>seen</u>   <u>further</u>   <u>than</u>   <u>others</u>   <u>it is by</u>
  10   11   3   2   1   4

<u>Standing</u>   <u>upon</u>   <u>the</u>   <u>shoulders</u>   <u>of</u>   <u>giants</u>
  5   6   7   12   9   8

$16 \div 2 =$ giants	$8 \div 2 =$ it is by	$24 \div 2 =$ shoulders	$22 \div 2 =$ seen	$6 \div 2 =$ further	$14 \div 2 =$ the
$10 \div 2 =$ standing	$4 \div 2 =$ than	$20 \div 2 =$ If I have	$2 \div 2 =$ others	$12 \div 2 =$ upon	$18 \div 2 =$ of

Who Stole My Number? In the equations below, there is a number missing! Fill in the missing numbers!

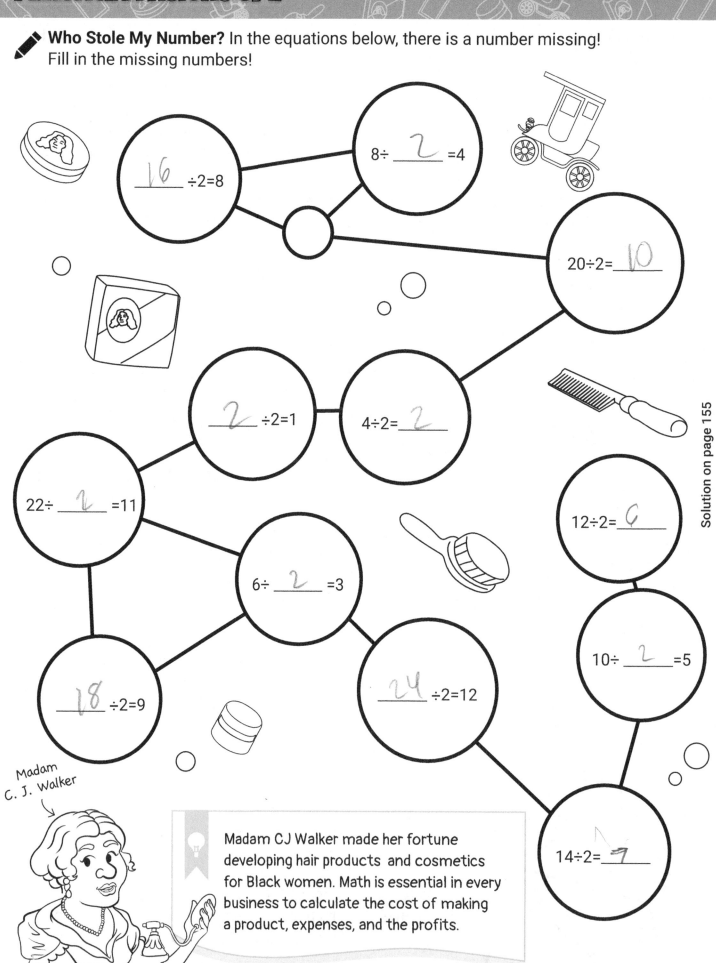

$16 \div 2 = 8$

$8 \div 2 = 4$

$20 \div 2 = 10$

$2 \div 2 = 1$

$4 \div 2 = 2$

$22 \div 2 = 11$

$12 \div 2 = 6$

$6 \div 2 = 3$

$18 \div 2 = 9$

$24 \div 2 = 12$

$10 \div 2 = 5$

$14 \div 2 = 7$

Solution on page 155

Madam C. J. Walker

Madam CJ Walker made her fortune developing hair products and cosmetics for Black women. Math is essential in every business to calculate the cost of making a product, expenses, and the profits.

✏ Complete the division problems in the color key to discover the colors to use in the picture.

Leonardo da Vinci created this painting sometime between 1503 and 1517. This masterpiece, called the Mona Lisa, is considered the most valuable work of art of all time. It is worth $650 million US dollars.

Solution on page 155

| 14÷2= | 24÷2= | 20÷2= | 18÷2= | 10÷2= | 4÷2= |
| Brown | Pink | Purple | Red | Light green | Light blue |

| 2÷2= | 22÷2= | 8÷2= | 6÷2= | 16÷2= | 12÷2= |
| Light skin color | Orange | Light gray | Blue | Yellow | Dark green |

PRACTICE DIVISIONS OF 2

✏️ **What's wrong?** Look at each problem carefully.
Circle only the problems that are correct.

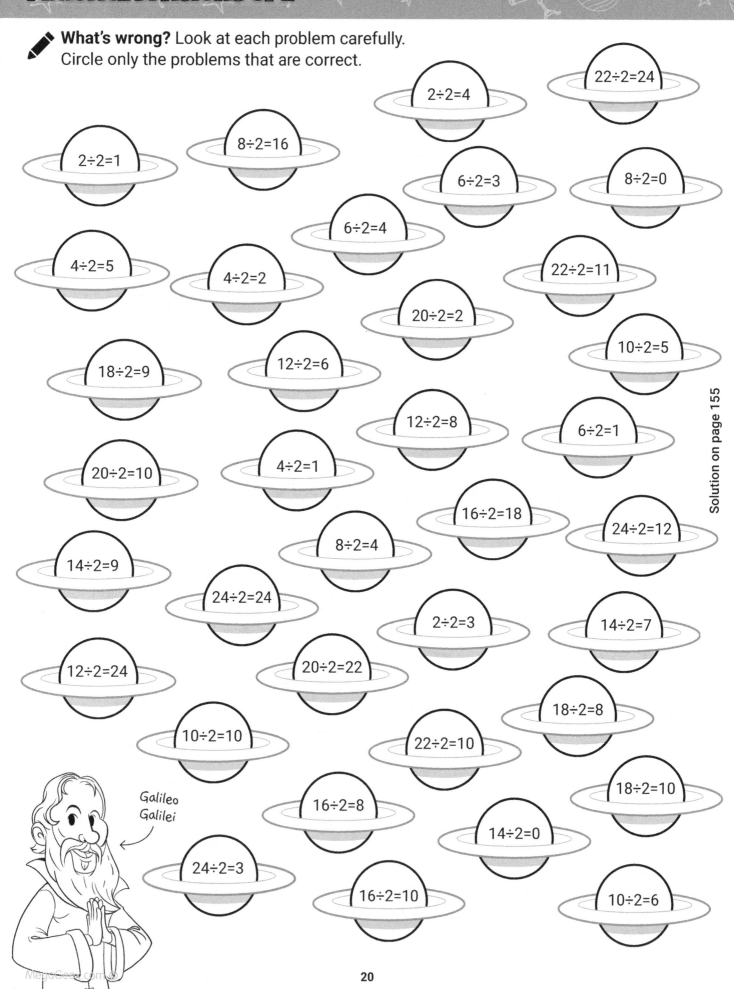

2÷2=4

22÷2=24

2÷2=1

8÷2=16

6÷2=3

8÷2=0

6÷2=4

4÷2=5

4÷2=2

22÷2=11

20÷2=2

10÷2=5

18÷2=9

12÷2=6

12÷2=8

6÷2=1

20÷2=10

4÷2=1

16÷2=18

24÷2=12

14÷2=9

8÷2=4

24÷2=24

2÷2=3

14÷2=7

12÷2=24

20÷2=22

18÷2=8

10÷2=10

22÷2=10

Galileo
Galilei

18÷2=10

16÷2=8

14÷2=0

24÷2=3

16÷2=10

10÷2=6

Solution on page 155

20

✏ Draw a line through the correct path of the maze by solving the division problems. The answer to the problem will show you the way and reveal the hidden item!

START

FINISH

Solution on page 155

What's the hidden item?

Rosalind Franklin

Rosalind Franklin developed better filters for gas masks. Her study of coal led to gas masks made with charcoal filters. This made the gas mask safer for soldiers in World War II.

MegaGeex.com ©

✎ **I have a problem!** During my travels on the HMS Beagle, I visited many countries and islands. I observed many animals. On one island I saw 10 different colorful birds in 2 days. How many birds did I see each of those days? Write the division problem and solve. Draw your answer if you want.

_____ ÷ _____ = _____

Day 1

Day 2

Charles Darwin

Solution on page 155

✏ Write the answers to each division problem on the puzzle frame. Color, cut, and glue the puzzle pieces to the frame with the matching answers to complete the puzzle.

Ada Lovelace

Solution on page 155

22÷2= ___

24÷2= ___

14÷2= ___

8÷2= ___

16÷2= ___

10÷2= ___

6÷2= ___

18÷2= ___

12÷2= ___

20÷2= ___

2÷2= ___

4÷2= ___

✏ **Grade the Megageex.**
Albert Einstein took a math test! Grade his answers carefully! ✗ or ✓

Solution on page 155

Part 1: Each correct answer earns Albert 5 points

○ 12÷2= 6 ○ 16÷2= 8 ○ 20÷2= 10

○ 8÷2= 5 ○ 2÷2= 1 ○ 14÷2= 8

○ 24÷2= 12 ○ 10÷2= 5 ○ 22÷2= 11

○ 6÷2= 3 ○ 8÷2= 2 ○ 4÷2= 3

Part 2: Challenge Problems! Each correct answer earns 10 points each..

Albert
Einstein

○ 8÷1= 8 ○ 11÷1= 11

○ 2x7= 12 ○ 7x8= 48

Calculate Albert Einstein's final grade!

Part 1 [ ] X **5** = [ ]
CORRECT ANSWERS   POINTS PER ANSWER

My grade is
_____

Part 2 [ ] X **10** = [ ]
CORRECT ANSWERS   POINTS PER ANSWER

Part 1 [ ] + **Part 2** [ ] = [ ]
POINTS   POINTS   GRADE

Albert Einstein went to school as a child, but teachers often thought he wasn't smart. However, he proved them wrong! He taught himself geometry and began his study of calculus at age 12.

What's wrong? Look at each problem carefully.
Circle only the problems that are correct.

33÷3=15

15÷3=5

15÷3=1

12÷3=1

33÷3=11

21÷3=8

6÷3=2

36÷3=12

15÷3=2

24÷3=8

3÷3 =0

18÷3=6

36÷3=15

33÷3=19

36÷3=10

3÷3 =2

12÷3=3

27÷3=8

6÷3=4

30÷3=13

21÷3=4

24÷3=18

18÷3=7

9÷3=8

30÷3=10

9÷3=4

12÷3=4

21÷3=7

27÷3=9

24÷3=17

30÷3=11

27÷3=6

9÷3=3

6÷3=1

3÷3 =1

18÷3=5

Wolfgang
Amadeus
Mozart

Solution on page 155

Solve the division problems. Then, color each pixel the correct color to reveal the image.

12÷3= Blue	24÷3= Gray	30÷3= Dark green	3÷3= White	36÷3= Purple	15÷3= Light orange
6÷3= Brown	18÷3= Yellow	9÷3= Green	27÷3= Light blue	33÷3= Dark brown	21÷3= Red

Solution on page 155

The Wright Flyer made the first successful powered flight in Kitty Hawk, North Carolina in 1903. The first flight lasted 12 seconds.

✏️ **I have a problem!** This year, I grew a bumper crop of sweet potatoes! I sold 40 bushels of sweet potatoes at the market. I still have 10 bushels left. There are 5 families that I would like to share the leftover bushels with. How many bushels will each family get? Write the division problem and solve. Draw a picture showing your answer if you want.

_____ ÷ _____ = _____

Solution on page 155

George Whashington Carver →

Draw a line through the correct path of the maze by solving the division problems. The answer to the problem will show you the way and reveal the hidden item!

Thomas Edison invented the first workable light bulb in 1879. Thomas Edison tried over 1000 times to find a filament that would burn for a long period of time. Edison's bamboo filament would light and burn for over 1000 hours.

What's the hidden item? _____

Solution on page 156

Thomas Edison

$15÷3$ 7 5

$24÷3$ 9 8 10

$12÷3$ 4 5

$27÷3$ 9 6 2

$33÷3$ 11 6 9 8

$6÷3$ 3

$3÷3$ 1 12

$9÷3$ 8 3 6

$30÷3$ 10 30

$21÷3$ 7 9 8

$18÷3$

FINISH

START

MegaGeex.com ©

Matching Game. Match the division problem on the left side of the page to its answer on the right side.

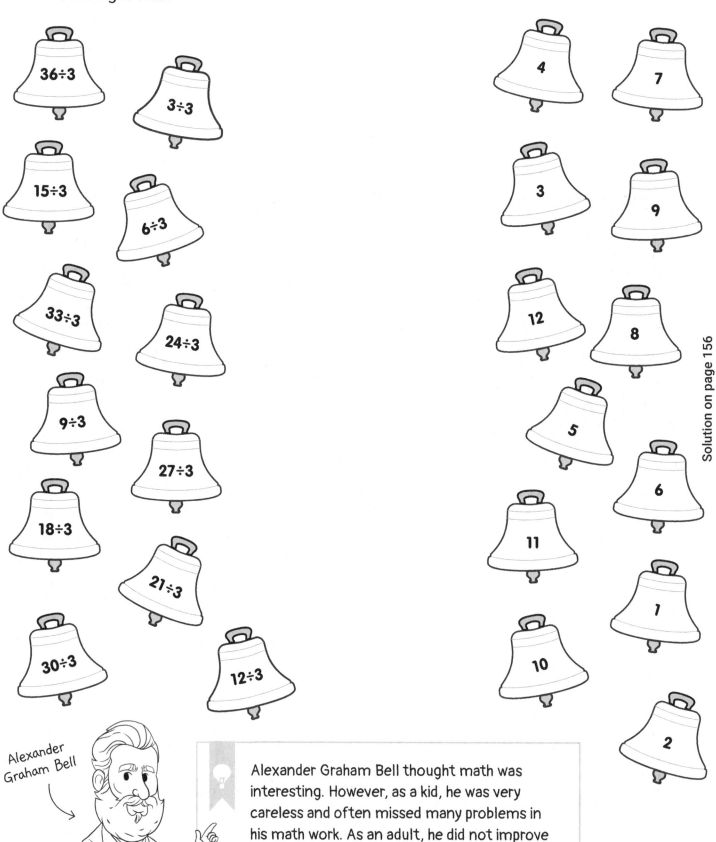

36÷3　　3÷3

15÷3　　6÷3

33÷3　　24÷3

9÷3　　27÷3

18÷3　　21÷3

30÷3　　12÷3

4　　7

3　　9

12　　8

5

6

11

1

10

2

Solution on page 156

Alexander Graham Bell

Alexander Graham Bell thought math was interesting. However, as a kid, he was very careless and often missed many problems in his math work. As an adult, he did not improve and he often made errors in his computations.

✎ Complete the division problems in the color key to discover the colors to use in the picture.

3÷3= Purple	15÷3= Green	27÷3= Yellow	6÷3= Orange
18÷3= Red	30÷3= Dark red	9÷3= Blue	21÷3= Dark purple
33÷3= Gray	12÷3= Brown	24÷3= Light green	36÷3= Pink

Solution on page 156

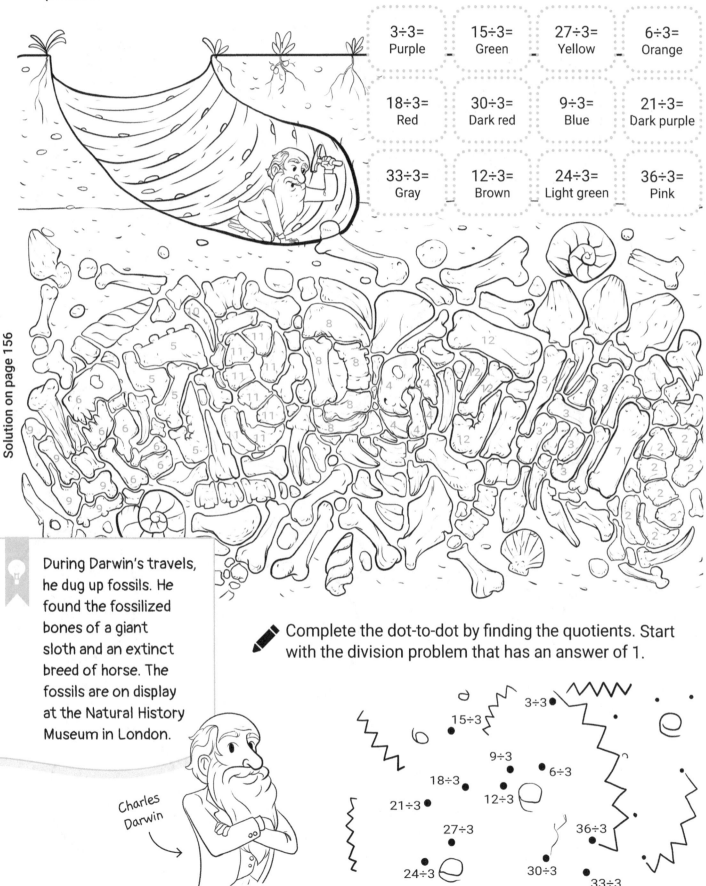

During Darwin's travels, he dug up fossils. He found the fossilized bones of a giant sloth and an extinct breed of horse. The fossils are on display at the Natural History Museum in London.

Charles Darwin

✎ Complete the dot-to-dot by finding the quotients. Start with the division problem that has an answer of 1.

3÷3
15÷3
9÷3
6÷3
18÷3
12÷3
21÷3
27÷3
36÷3
24÷3
30÷3
33÷3

Who Stole My Number? In the equations below, there is a number missing! Fill in the missing numbers!

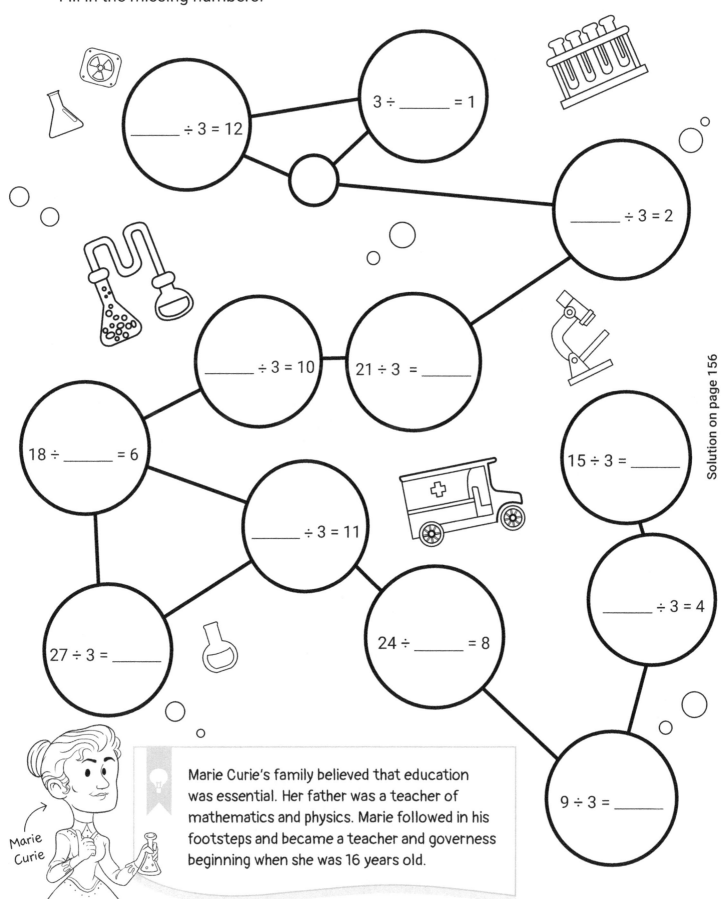

_____ ÷ 3 = 12

3 ÷ _____ = 1

_____ ÷ 3 = 2

_____ ÷ 3 = 10

21 ÷ 3 = _____

18 ÷ _____ = 6

15 ÷ 3 = _____

_____ ÷ 3 = 11

_____ ÷ 3 = 4

27 ÷ 3 = _____

24 ÷ _____ = 8

9 ÷ 3 = _____

Solution on page 156

Marie Curie's family believed that education was essential. Her father was a teacher of mathematics and physics. Marie followed in his footsteps and became a teacher and governess beginning when she was 16 years old.

Marie Curie

MegaGeex.com ©

32

✏️ **Grade the Megageex.**
The Wright Brothers took a math test! Grade his answers carefully! ✗ or ✓

Part 1: Each correct answer earns the brothers 7 points.

◯ 36÷3= 12

◯ 12÷3= 4

◯ 33÷3= 10

◯ 3÷3= 1

◯ 24÷3= 8

◯ 21÷3= 7

◯ 15÷3= 4

◯ 9÷3= 3

◯ 30÷3= 10

◯ 27÷3= 9

◯ 6÷3= 2

◯ 18÷3= 5

Solution on page 156

Part 2: Challenge Problems! Each correct answer earns 4 points each.

◯ 18÷2= 9

◯ 14÷2= 8

◯ 6÷2= 3

◯ 2÷2= 1

The Wright Brothers

Calculate the brothers' final grade!

Part 1 ▭ X **7** = ▭   **Our grade is** ____
CORRECT ANSWERS   POINTS PER ANSWER

Part 2 ▭ X **4** = ▭
CORRECT ANSWERS   POINTS PER ANSWER

Part 1 ▭ + **Part 2** ▭ = ▭
POINTS   POINTS   GRADE

💡 Wilbur and Orville Wright had natural technical skills. Neither went to college, but both studied algebra, geometry, and trigonometry in high school. Wilbur made very high grades in these subjects.

Tesla coils produce high-voltage, low-current electricity. Tesla built these, and loved creating beautiful currents of energy with them. The coils were used in many of his other inventions.

9÷3= ___	6÷3= ___
24÷3= ___	36÷3= ___
30÷3= ___	18÷3= ___
21÷3= ___	3÷3= ___
27÷3= ___	15÷3= ___
33÷3= ___	12÷3= ___

Solution on page 156

Write the answer to each division problem on the puzzle frame. Color, cut, and glue the puzzle pieces to the frame with the matching answers to complete the puzzle.

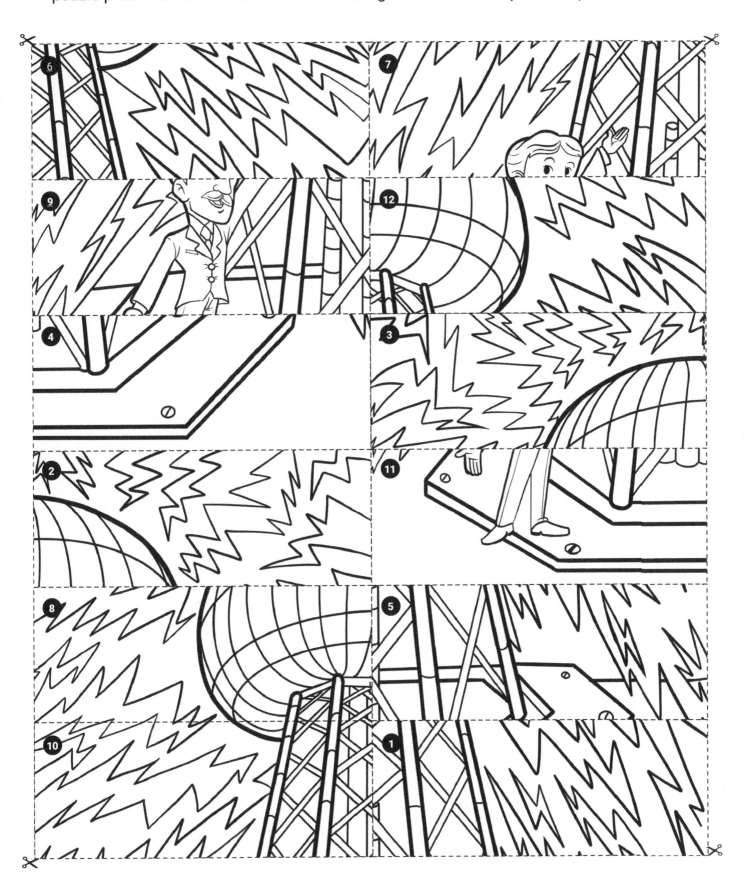

Who Stole My Number? In the equations below, there is a number missing! Fill in the missing numbers!

Solution on page 156

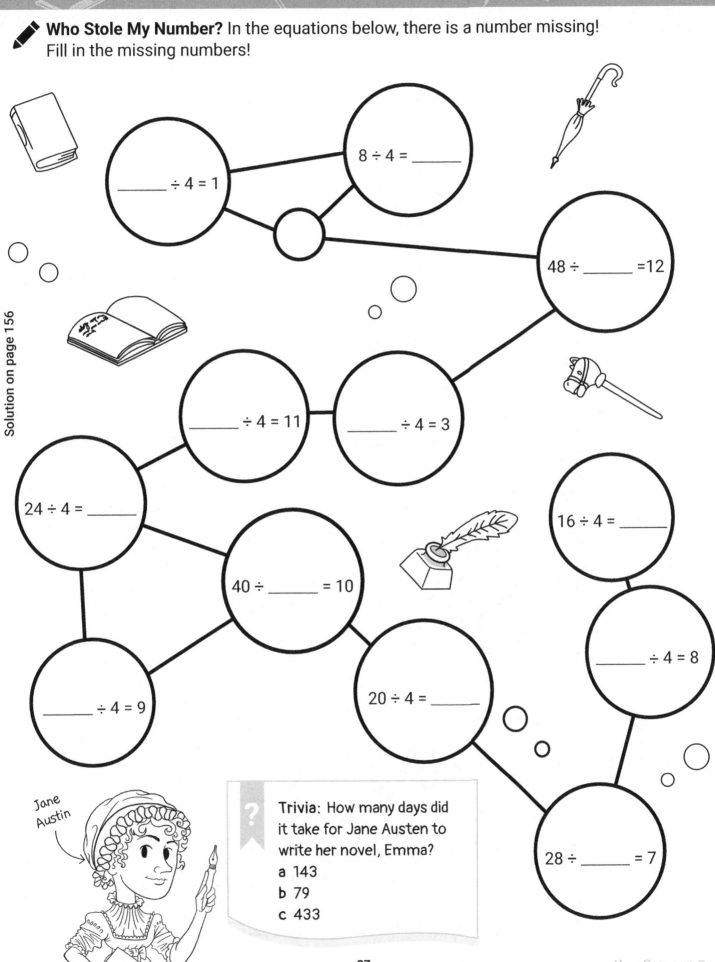

_____ ÷ 4 = 1

8 ÷ 4 = _____

48 ÷ _____ = 12

_____ ÷ 4 = 11

_____ ÷ 4 = 3

24 ÷ 4 = _____

40 ÷ _____ = 10

16 ÷ 4 = _____

_____ ÷ 4 = 9

_____ ÷ 4 = 8

20 ÷ 4 = _____

28 ÷ _____ = 7

Jane Austin

Trivia: How many days did it take for Jane Austen to write her novel, Emma?
a 143
b 79
c 433

Complete the dot-to-dot by finding the quotients. Start with the division problem that has an answer of 1.

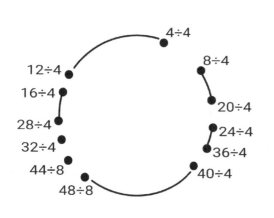

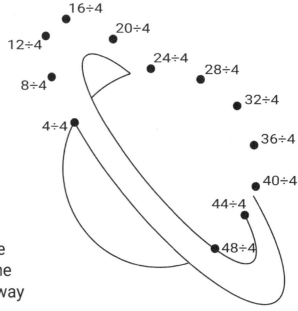

Solution on page 156

 Draw a line through the correct path of the maze by solving the division problems. The answer to the problem will show you the way and reveal the hidden item!

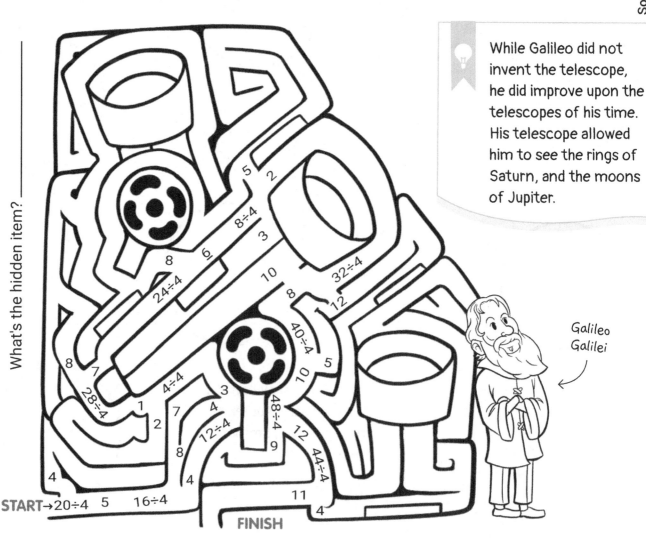

While Galileo did not invent the telescope, he did improve upon the telescopes of his time. His telescope allowed him to see the rings of Saturn, and the moons of Jupiter.

Galileo Galilei

✏️ **Matching Game.** Match the division problem on the left side of the page to its answer on the right side.

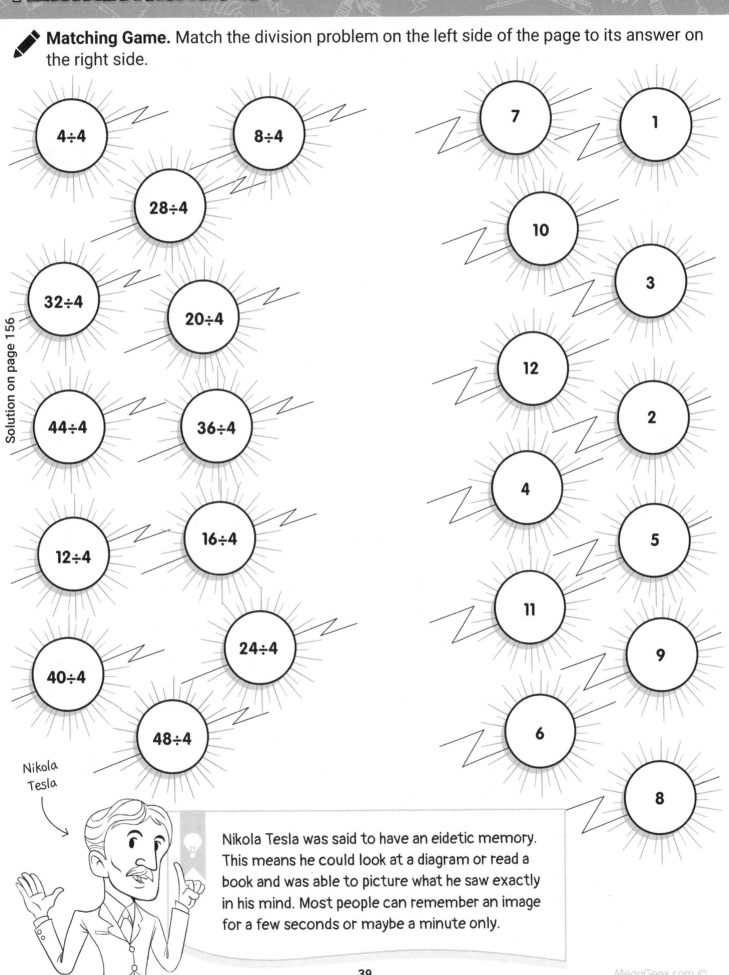

Solution on page 156

4÷4   8÷4   28÷4

32÷4   20÷4

44÷4   36÷4

12÷4   16÷4

40÷4   24÷4

48÷4

7   1

10   3

12

4   2

11   5

6   9

8

Nikola Tesla

Nikola Tesla was said to have an eidetic memory. This means he could look at a diagram or read a book and was able to picture what he saw exactly in his mind. Most people can remember an image for a few seconds or maybe a minute only.

✏️ **What's wrong?** Look at each problem carefully. Circle only the problems that are correct.

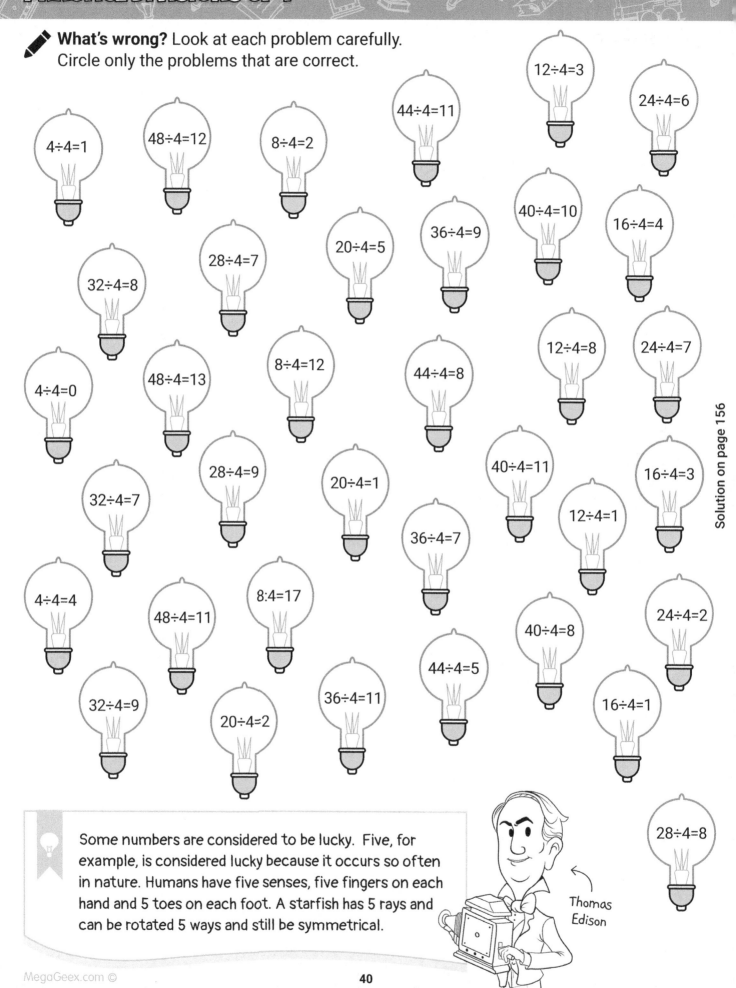

4÷4=1

48÷4=12

8÷4=2

44÷4=11

12÷4=3

24÷4=6

32÷4=8

28÷4=7

20÷4=5

36÷4=9

40÷4=10

16÷4=4

4÷4=0

48÷4=13

8÷4=12

44÷4=8

12÷4=8

24÷4=7

32÷4=7

28÷4=9

20÷4=1

36÷4=7

40÷4=11

12÷4=1

16÷4=3

4÷4=4

48÷4=11

8:4=17

40÷4=8

44÷4=5

24÷4=2

32÷4=9

20÷4=2

36÷4=11

16÷4=1

28÷4=8

Solution on page 156

💡 Some numbers are considered to be lucky. Five, for example, is considered lucky because it occurs so often in nature. Humans have five senses, five fingers on each hand and 5 toes on each foot. A starfish has 5 rays and can be rotated 5 ways and still be symmetrical.

Thomas Edison

Write the answer to each division problem on the puzzle frame. Color, cut, and glue the puzzle pieces to the frame with the matching answers to complete the puzzle.

Wolfgang Amadeus Mozart's father taught him to play the piano when he was 4 years old. Mozart often composed music using it, even music for other instruments!

Solution on page 156

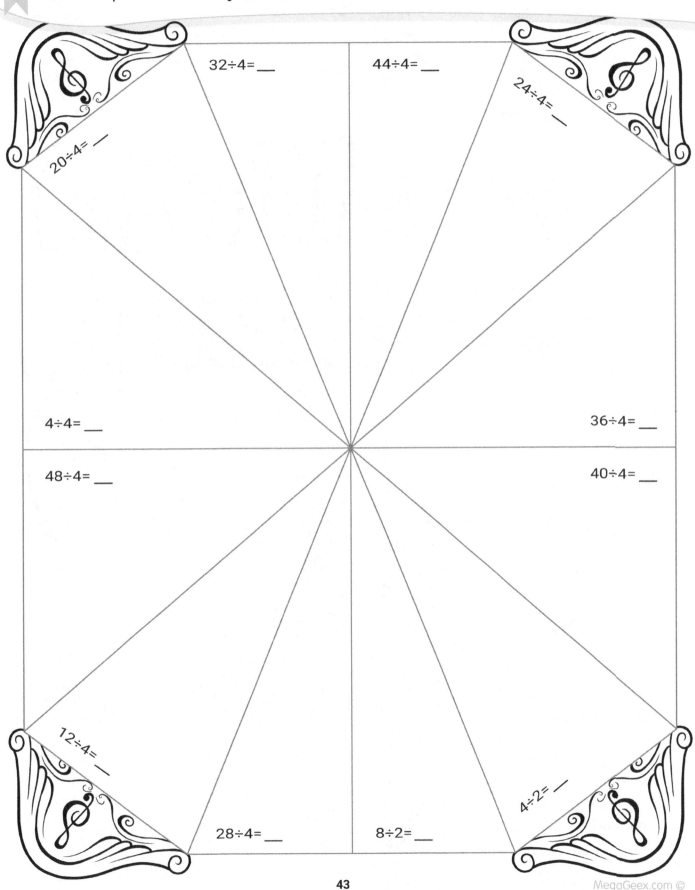

$32 \div 4 =$ ___

$44 \div 4 =$ ___

$24 \div 4 =$ ___

$20 \div 4 =$ ___

$4 \div 4 =$ ___

$36 \div 4 =$ ___

$48 \div 4 =$ ___

$40 \div 4 =$ ___

$12 \div 4 =$ ___

$4 \div 2 =$ ___

$28 \div 4 =$ ___

$8 \div 2 =$ ___

Complete the division problems in the color key to discover the colors to use in the picture.

28÷4= Dark skin color	36÷4= Black	44÷4= Yellow	16÷4= Blue	8÷4= Turquoise	24÷4= Light blue
4÷4= Pink	32÷4= Red	20÷4= Orange	40÷4= Gray	12÷4= Green	48÷4= Purple

Positive minding positive RESULTS

Madam C. J. Walker

Positive thinking led to great success for Madam CJ Walker. With her hair and cosmetics line for Black women, she became a millionaire.

Solution on page 156

✏️ **I have a problem!** My father was the famous poet Lord Byron. He wrote a book with 16 poems. I will read all of the poems in 4 days. How many poems do I need to read each day to complete the book in 4 days? Write the division problem and solve. Draw a picture showing your answer if you want.

Solution on page 157

_____ ÷ _____ = _____

Day 1

Day 2

Day 3

Day 4

Ada Lovelace

MegaGeex.com ©

Solve the problems in the picture. Then, color by number.

| 7 = Red | 4 = Pink | 10 = Purple | 8 = Yellow | 12 = Green | 6 = Dark blue |
| 1 = Blue | 3 = Green | 9 = Turquoise | 2 = Orange | 11 = Blue | 5 = Lilac |

Alan Turing's Enigma machine was used to decode secret messages from Nazi Germany. The messages helped the Allied Forces win World War II.

Solution on page 157

Grade the Megageex

Isaac Newton took a math test! Grade his answers carefully! ✗ or ✓

Solution on page 157

Part 1: Each correct answer earns Newton 5 points.

◯ 4÷4= 1   ◯ 12÷4= 3   ◯ 36÷4= 9

◯ 48÷4= 11   ◯ 24÷4= 6   ◯ 20÷4= 5

◯ 8÷4= 2   ◯ 40÷4= 10   ◯ 32÷4= 8

◯ 44÷4= 11   ◯ 16÷4= 4   ◯ 28÷4= 7

Part 2: Challenge Problems! Each correct answer earns 10 points each.

◯ 12÷3= 4   ◯ 8÷2= 3

◯ 18÷3= 5   ◯ 27÷3= 9

Isaac
Newton

Calculate Isaac Newton's final grade!

Part 1 [ ] **X** **5** **=** [ ]
CORRECT ANSWERS   POINTS PER ANSWER

Part 2 [ ] **X** **10** **=** [ ]
CORRECT ANSWERS   POINTS PER ANSWER

My grade is

_____

Part 1 [ ] **+** **Part 2** [ ] **=** [ ]
POINTS   POINTS   GRADE

Isaac Newton "invented" calculus. With calculus, you can study the motion of the stars and planets, weather patterns, sound and light waves, and more!

Matching Game. Match the division problem on the left side of the page to its answer on the right side.

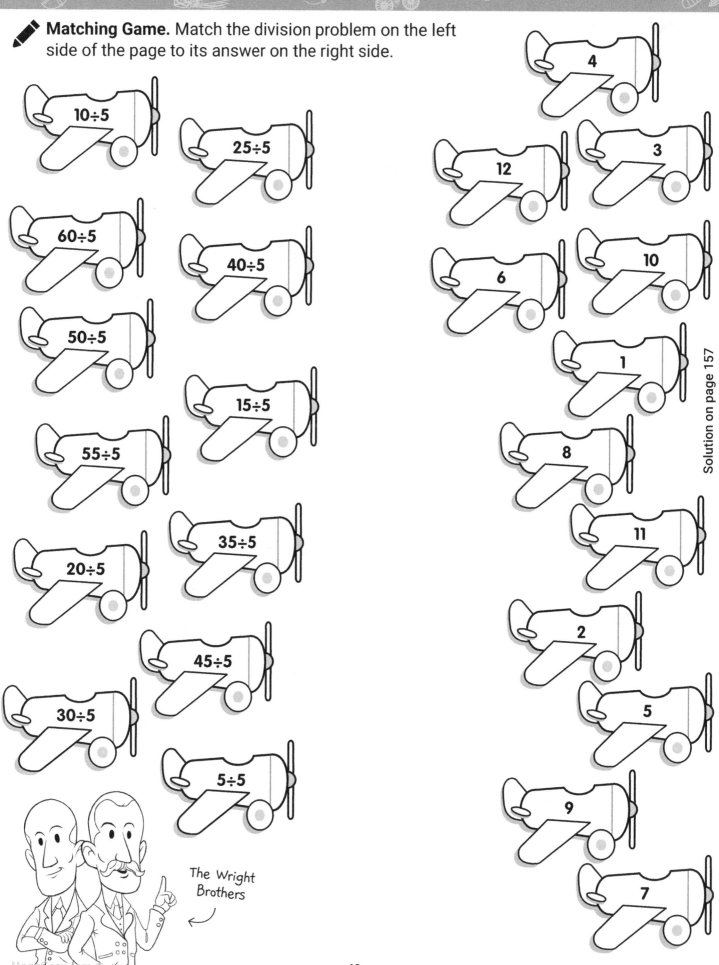

10÷5

25÷5

60÷5

40÷5

50÷5

15÷5

55÷5

35÷5

20÷5

45÷5

30÷5

5÷5

4

12

3

6

10

1

8

11

2

5

9

7

The Wright Brothers

Solution on page 157

48

✏️ Complete the dot-to-dot by finding the quotients. Start with the division problem that has an answer of 1.

💡 Alexander Graham Bell invented an early hydrofoil, a sort of water-skimming boat that operates in a similar way to a plane. The hydrofoil could travel over 70 mph or 61 knots.

Solution on page 157

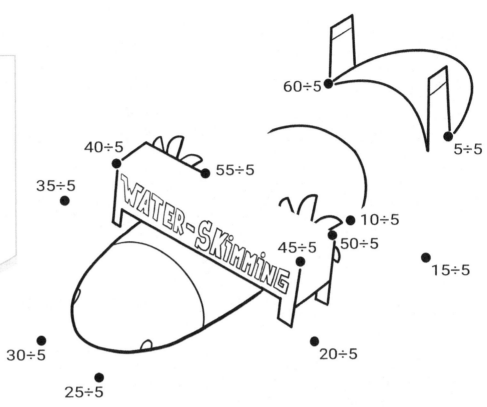

✏️ Find the answers to each division problem. Write the word(s) on the lines with the matching answers to see the message.

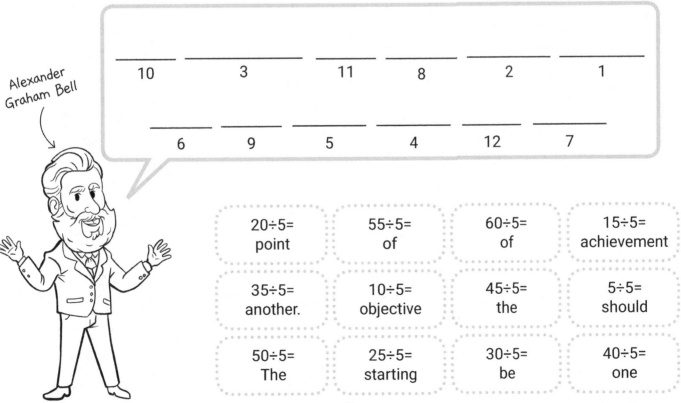

Alexander Graham Bell

```
____  ____  ____  ____  ____  ____
 10    3     11    8     2     1

____  ____  ____  ____  ____  ____
 6     9     5     4     12    7
```

20÷5= point	55÷5= of	60÷5= of	15÷5= achievement
35÷5= another.	10÷5= objective	45÷5= the	5÷5= should
50÷5= The	25÷5= starting	30÷5= be	40÷5= one

MegaGeex.com ©

What's wrong? Look at each problem carefully. Circle only the problems that are correct.

5÷5=1
10÷5=2
35÷5=8
5÷5=2
55÷5=11

15÷5=3
20÷5=4
45÷5=8
15÷5=1
50÷5=10

10÷5=5
30÷5=6
25÷5=7
30÷5=9
20÷5=4

15÷5=4
25÷5=3
10÷5=3
40÷5=5
45÷5=4

60÷5=14
40÷5=8
20÷5=2
25÷5=5
35÷5=8

55÷5=10
60÷5=12
5÷5=0
35÷5=7
50÷5=8

50÷5=11
55÷5=12
60÷5=10
40÷5=4

45÷5=9
30÷5=10

Charles Darwin

Solution on page 157

MegaGeex.com ©

50

Complete the division problems in the color key to discover the colors to use in the picture.

Solution on page 157

George Whashington Carver

35÷5= Purple	10÷5= Light green	45÷5= Orange	20÷5= Pink	25÷5= Light red	55÷5= Green
5÷5= Red	40÷5= Light pink	15÷5= Blue	50÷5= Yellow	30÷5= Brown	60÷5= Gray

✎ **I have a problem!** I discovered four moons of Jupiter in 1610. Now astronomers know that Jupiter has 79 moons! If you have five days to visit 20 of Jupiter's moon, how many moons can you visit each day? You will visit the same number of moons each day. Write the division problem and solve. Draw a picture showing your answer if you want.

_____ ÷ _____ = _____

Day 1

Day 2

Day 3

Day 4

Day 5

Galileo Galilei

Solution on page 157

✎ Complete the dot-to-dot by finding the quotients. Start with the division problem that has an answer of 1.

Looking at pictures of Einstein, he is often pictured with wild looking hair. Some theorize that he was too busy to comb it often or visit a barber.

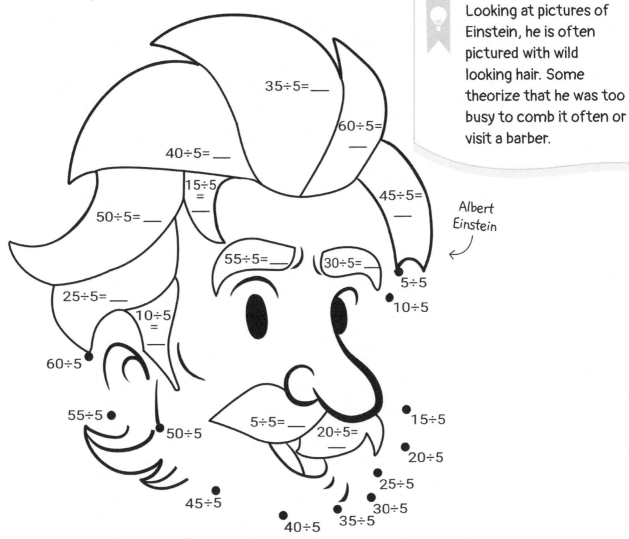

$35 \div 5 =$ ___

$60 \div 5 =$ ___

$40 \div 5 =$ ___

$15 \div 5 =$ ___

$45 \div 5 =$ ___

$50 \div 5 =$ ___

$55 \div 5 =$ ___

$30 \div 5 =$ ___

$5 \div 5$

$10 \div 5$

$25 \div 5 =$ ___

$10 \div 5 =$ ___

$60 \div 5$

Albert Einstein

$55 \div 5$

$50 \div 5$

$5 \div 5 =$ ___

$20 \div 5 =$ ___

$15 \div 5$

$20 \div 5$

$25 \div 5$

$45 \div 5$

$40 \div 5$

$35 \div 5$

$30 \div 5$

Solution on page 157

✎ Color, then cut, the pieces of Einstein's hair at the bottom of the page. Glue them to the correct spaces on Einsteins head to complete the picture.

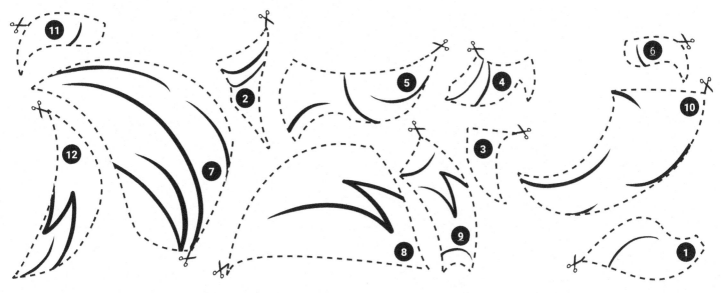

Who Stole My Number? In the equations below, there is a number missing! Fill in the missing numbers.

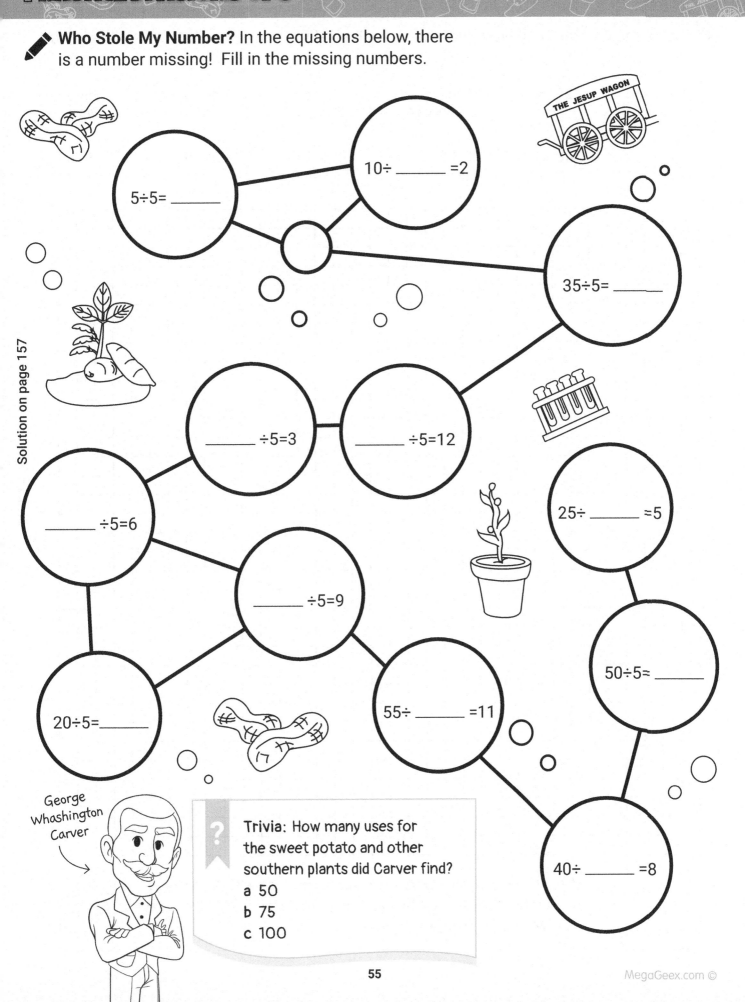

$5 \div 5 =$ _____

$10 \div$ _____ $= 2$

THE JESUP WAGON

$35 \div 5 =$ _____

_____ $\div 5 = 3$

_____ $\div 5 = 12$

$25 \div$ _____ $= 5$

_____ $\div 5 = 6$

_____ $\div 5 = 9$

$20 \div 5 =$ _____

$55 \div$ _____ $= 11$

$50 \div 5 =$ _____

$40 \div$ _____ $= 8$

George Whashington Carver

? Trivia: How many uses for the sweet potato and other southern plants did Carver find?
a 50
b 75
c 100

Solve the division problems. Then, color each pixel the correct color to reveal the image.

35÷5= Light green	25÷5= Black	45÷5= Dark blue
20÷5= Orange	10÷5= Yellow	55÷5= Brown
5÷5= White	40÷5= Gray	15÷5= Light skin color
60÷5= Dark brown	30÷5= Red	50÷5= Green

Solution on page 157

Marie Curie discovered two new elements and was the first woman to win the Nobel Prize twice. Her work on radioactivity led to better X-rays and helped doctors save many lives.

Grade the Megageex
Jane Austen took a math test! Grade her answers carefully! ✗ or ✓

Part 1: Each correct answer earns Jane 4 points.

( ) 60÷5= 12   ( ) 30÷5= 6   ( ) 25÷5= 5

( ) 15÷5= 5   ( ) 50÷5= 10   ( ) 40÷5= 8

( ) 20÷5= 4   ( ) 45÷5= 9

( ) 55÷5= 11   ( ) 10÷5= 2

Part 2: Challenge Problems! Each correct answer earns 12 points each.

( ) 35÷7= 6   ( ) 5÷5= 1   ( ) 20÷4= 5

( ) 15÷3= 6   ( ) 10÷2= 5

Jane Austin

Calculate Jane's final grade!

Part 1 [ ] X **4** = [ ]
CORRECT ANSWERS   POINTS PER ANSWER

Part 2 [ ] X **12** = [ ]
CORRECT ANSWERS   POINTS PER ANSWER

My grade is
_____

Part 1 [ ] + **Part 2** [ ] = [ ]
POINTS   POINTS   GRADE

PRACTICE DIVISIONS OF 6

✏️ **Matching Game**. Match the division problem on the left side of the page to its answer on the right side.

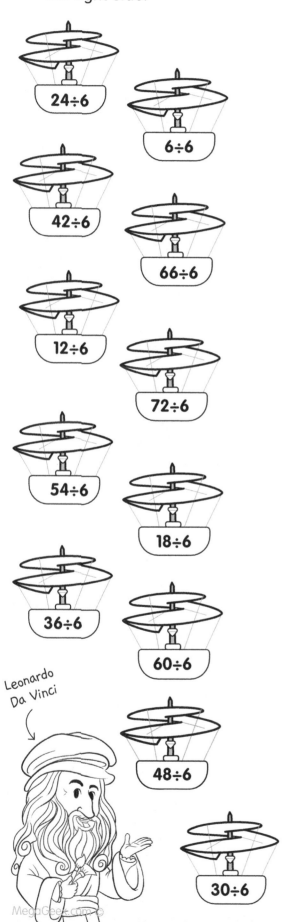

24÷6

6÷6

42÷6

66÷6

12÷6

72÷6

54÷6

18÷6

36÷6

60÷6

Leonardo Da Vinci

48÷6

30÷6

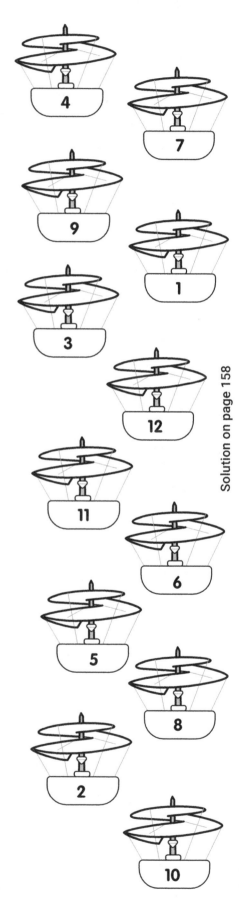

4

7

9

1

3

12

11

6

5

8

2

10

Solution on page 158

MegaGeek.com ©

Complete the dot-to-dot by finding the quotients. Start with the division problem that has an answer of 1.

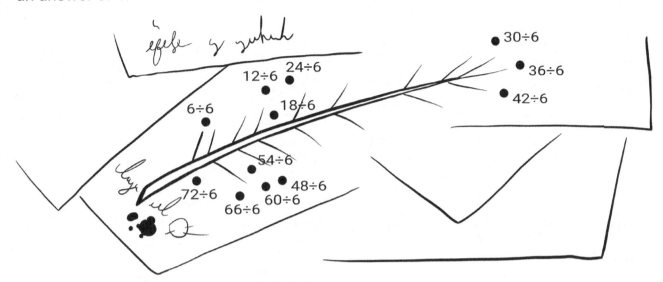

Complete the division problems in th color key to discover the colors to use in the picture.

Solution on page 158

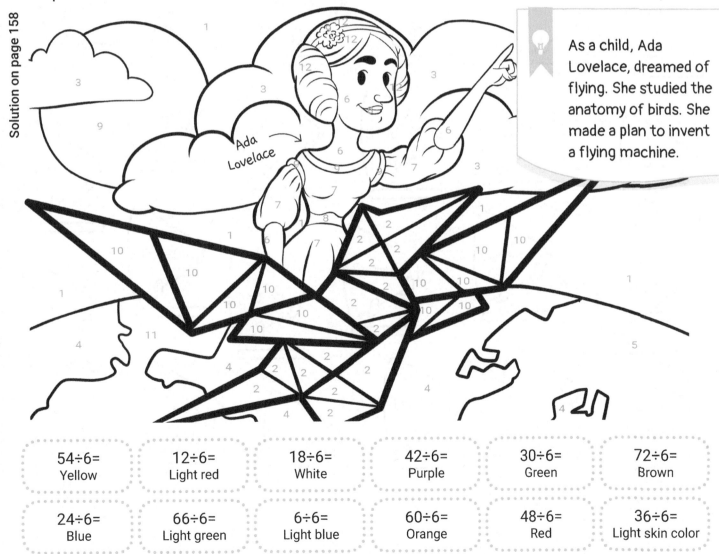

Ada Lovelace

As a child, Ada Lovelace, dreamed of flying. She studied the anatomy of birds. She made a plan to invent a flying machine.

54÷6= Yellow	12÷6= Light red	18÷6= White	42÷6= Purple	30÷6= Green	72÷6= Brown
24÷6= Blue	66÷6= Light green	6÷6= Light blue	60÷6= Orange	48÷6= Red	36÷6= Light skin color

✏️ **What's wrong?** Look at each problem carefully. Circle only the problems that are correct.

6÷6=1

30÷6=5

12÷6=4

60÷6=16

72÷6=14

30÷6=6

42÷6=7

24÷6=4

6÷6=0

18÷6=7

54÷6=11

24÷6=5

72÷6=12

36÷6=6

42÷6=7

36÷6=4

6÷6=2

36÷6=8

54÷6=9

48÷6=8

72÷6=13

48÷6=9

42÷6=8

48÷6=6

12÷6=2

54÷6=16

30÷6=2

12÷6=4

60÷6=12

18÷6=5

66÷6=11

66÷6=1

18÷6=3

24÷6=8

66÷6=10

Alexander
Graham Bell

Solution on page 158

MegaGeex.com ©

60

✎ Draw a line through the correct path of the maze by solving the division problems. The answer to the problem will show you the way and reveal the hidden item!

Charles Darwin

Charles Darwin studied geology too. He used a pickaxe to dig and find rocks.

Solution on page 158

What's the hidden item? _____

✎ Complete the division problems in the color key. Find the numbers hidden in the maze and color the picture using the color indicated below.

42÷6= Light red	24÷6= Pink	54÷6= Light blue	12÷6= Purple	30÷6= Gray	72÷6= Dark green
66÷6= Blue	48÷6= Red	18÷6= Green	60÷6= Orange	6÷6= Yellow	36÷6= Brown

PRACTICE DIVISIONS OF 6

Who Stole My Number? In the equations below, there is a number missing!
Fill in the missing numbers!

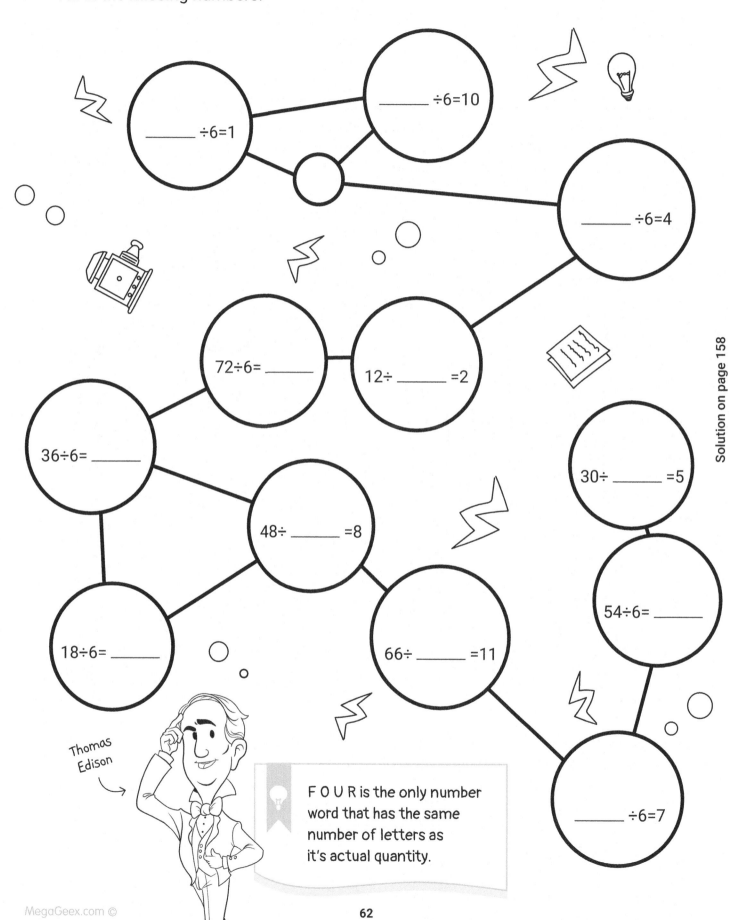

$\_\_\_\_ \div 6 = 1$

$\_\_\_\_ \div 6 = 10$

$\_\_\_\_ \div 6 = 4$

$72 \div 6 = \_\_\_\_$

$12 \div \_\_\_\_ = 2$

$36 \div 6 = \_\_\_\_$

$30 \div \_\_\_\_ = 5$

$48 \div \_\_\_\_ = 8$

$18 \div 6 = \_\_\_\_$

$66 \div \_\_\_\_ = 11$

$54 \div 6 = \_\_\_\_$

$\_\_\_\_ \div 6 = 7$

Solution on page 158

Thomas
Edison

F O U R is the only number
word that has the same
number of letters as
it's actual quantity.

Write the answer to each division problem on the puzzle frame. Color, cut, and glue the puzzle pieces to the frame with the matching answers to complete the puzzle.

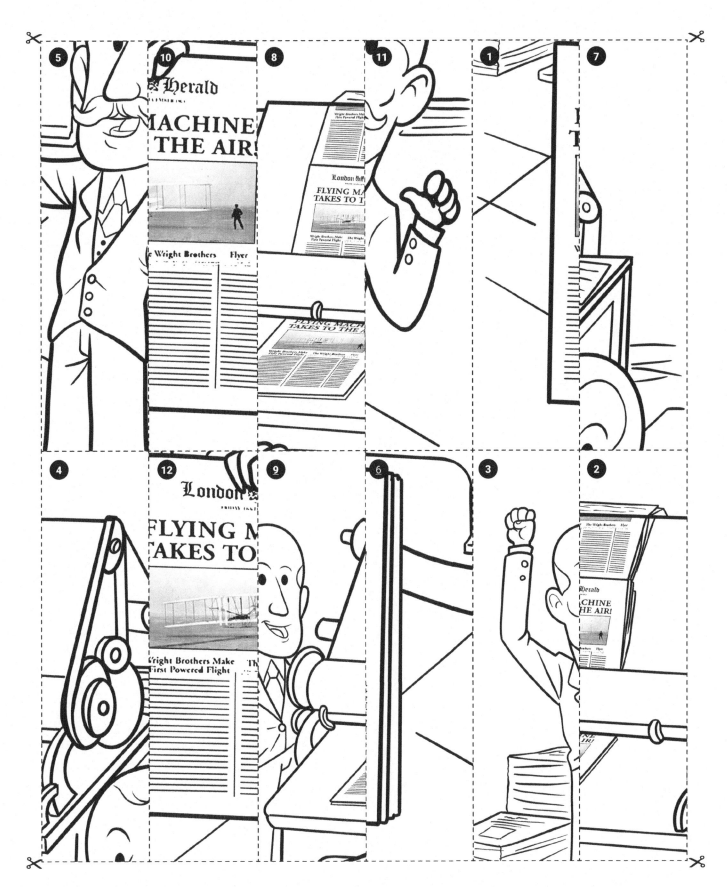

Before the Wright Brothers completed the first airplane flight, they were printers. Over a period of several years, they printed different publications including a weekly newspaper.

Solution on page 158

18÷6=___	54÷6=___	48÷6=___	12÷6=___	24÷6=___	42÷6=___
6÷6=___	72÷6=___	60÷6=___	36÷6=___	30÷6=___	66÷6=___

✎ **I have a problem!** I love to run! In fact, I ran as fast as Olympic athletes in the many marathons that I competed in. I run to work every day. In 6 days, I ran 30 miles. How many miles* did I run each day?
Write the division problem and solve. Draw a picture showing your answer if you want.

_____ ÷ _____ = _____

Day 1

Day 2

Day 3

Day 4

Day 5

Day 6

* In some countries, distance is measured in kilometers rather than miles. A mile is equal to 1.6 kilometers.

Alan Turing

Solution on page 158

MegaGeex.com ©

Madam CJ Walker is considered the first American self-made millionaire. She made her fortune creating hair care products and cosmetics for Black women.

Solution on page 158

Complete the division problems in the color key to discover the colors to use in the picture.

$42 \div 6 =$	$30 \div 6 =$	$18 \div 6 =$	$60 \div 6 =$	$12 \div 6 =$	$72 \div 6 =$
Red	Light red	Light blue	Gray	Dark skin color	Green

$6 \div 6 =$	$48 \div 6 =$	$54 \div 6 =$	$24 \div 6 =$	$66 \div 6 =$	$36 \div 6 =$
Purple	Blue	Pink	Yellow	Orange	Light green

Grade the Megageex
Nikola Tesla took a math test! Grade his answers carefully! or ✓

Part 1: Each correct answer earns Nikola 5 points

○ 30÷6= 5   ○ 6÷6=1   ○ 54÷6= 9

○ 72÷6= 12   ○ 36÷6= 5   ○ 42÷6= 7

○ 60÷6= 10   ○ 18÷6= 3   ○ 66÷6= 11

○ 24÷6= 4   ○ 48÷6= 8   ○ 12÷6= 2

Part 2: Challenge Problems! Each correct answer earns Nikola 10 points

○ 30÷5= 6   ○ 24÷4= 4

○ 18÷3= 6   ○ 12÷2= 3

Nikola Tesla

Solution on page 158

Calculate Nikola Tesla's final grade!

Part 1 [ ] X **5** = [ ]
CORRECT ANSWERS   POINTS PER ANSWER

My grade is
_____

Part 2 [ ] X **10** = [ ]
CORRECT ANSWERS   POINTS PER ANSWER

Part 1 [ ] + **Part 2** [ ] = [ ]
POINTS   POINTS   GRADE

Matching Game. Match the division problem on the left side of the page to its answer on the right side.

Solution on page 158

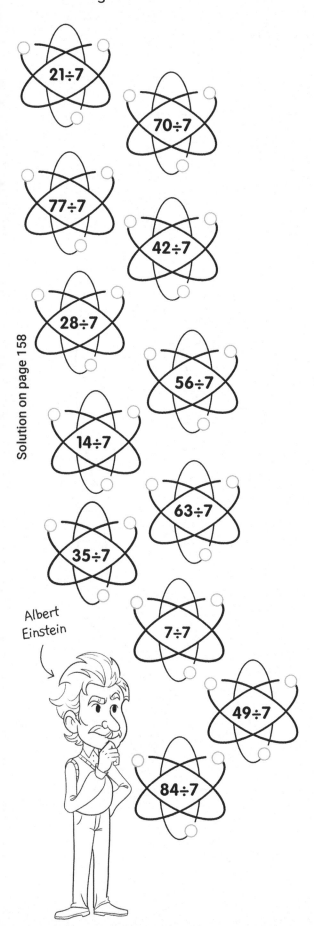

Albert Einstein

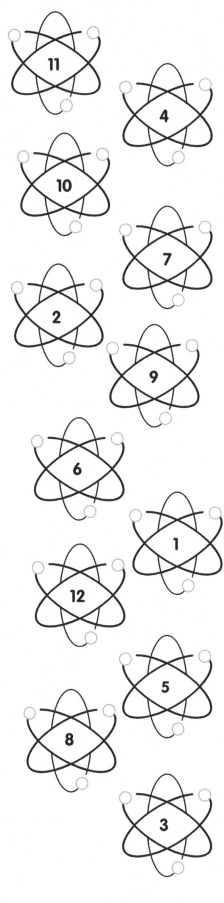

MegaGeex.com ©

Leonardo studied many things but now he needs rest! Help him through the maze of his interests and inventions. Solve each problem on the correct path so he can sleep. Start with the problem that has an answer of 1.

Leonardo Da Vinci

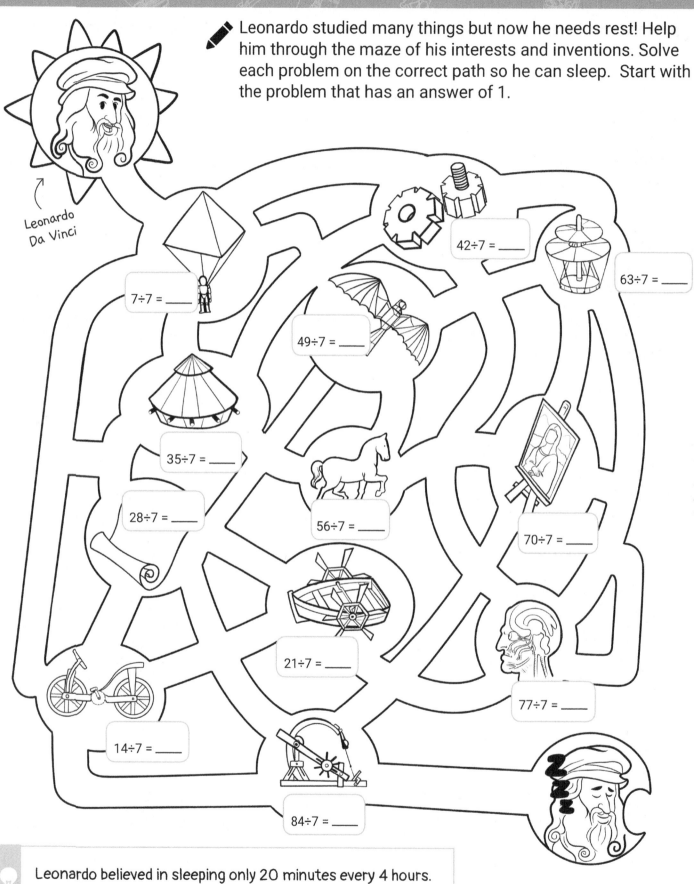

$42 \div 7 =$ _____

$63 \div 7 =$ _____

$7 \div 7 =$ _____

$49 \div 7 =$ _____

$35 \div 7 =$ _____

$28 \div 7 =$ _____

$56 \div 7 =$ _____

$70 \div 7 =$ _____

$21 \div 7 =$ _____

$77 \div 7 =$ _____

$14 \div 7 =$ _____

$84 \div 7 =$ _____

Solution on page 158

Leonardo believed in sleeping only 20 minutes every 4 hours. Many refer to this schedule as "the sleep of geniuses."

What's wrong? Look at each problem carefully. Circle only the problems that are correct.

7÷7=1

84÷7=12

63÷7=8

7÷7=4

7÷7=0

77÷7=11

63÷7=9

14÷7=4

63÷7=6

77÷7=12

84÷7=14

56÷7=8

14÷7=2

70÷7=8

14÷7=1

56÷7=2

42÷7=6

70÷7=10

77÷7=10

70÷7=12

42÷7=4

28÷7=4

35÷7=5

35÷7=3

21÷7=5

28÷7=8

49÷7=7

21÷7=3

49÷7=9

28÷7=6

49÷7=6

21÷7=2

35÷7=7

42÷7=8

Rosalind Franklin

84÷7=16

Solution on page 158

Who Stole My Number? In the equations below, there is a number missing! Fill in the missing numbers!

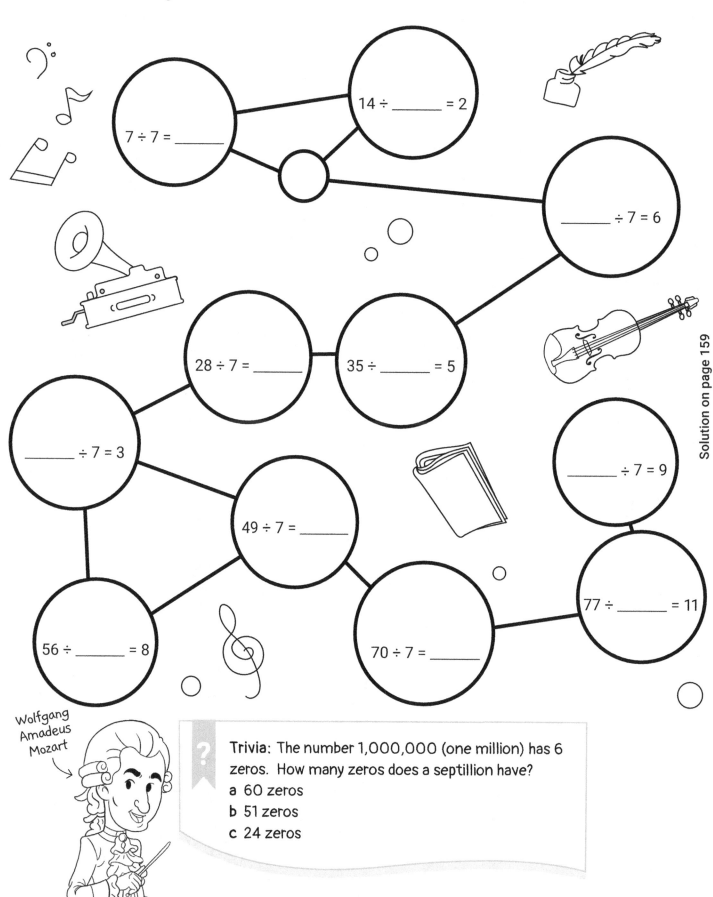

$7 \div 7 =$ _____

$14 \div$ _____ $= 2$

_____ $\div 7 = 6$

$28 \div 7 =$ _____

$35 \div$ _____ $= 5$

_____ $\div 7 = 3$

_____ $\div 7 = 9$

$49 \div 7 =$ _____

$56 \div$ _____ $= 8$

$70 \div 7 =$ _____

$77 \div$ _____ $= 11$

Solution on page 159

Wolfgang Amadeus Mozart

?

Trivia: The number 1,000,000 (one million) has 6 zeros. How many zeros does a septillion have?

a 60 zeros

b 51 zeros

c 24 zeros

✏️ Write the answer to each division problem on the puzzle frame. Color, cut, and glue the puzzle pieces to the frame with the matching answers to complete the puzzle.

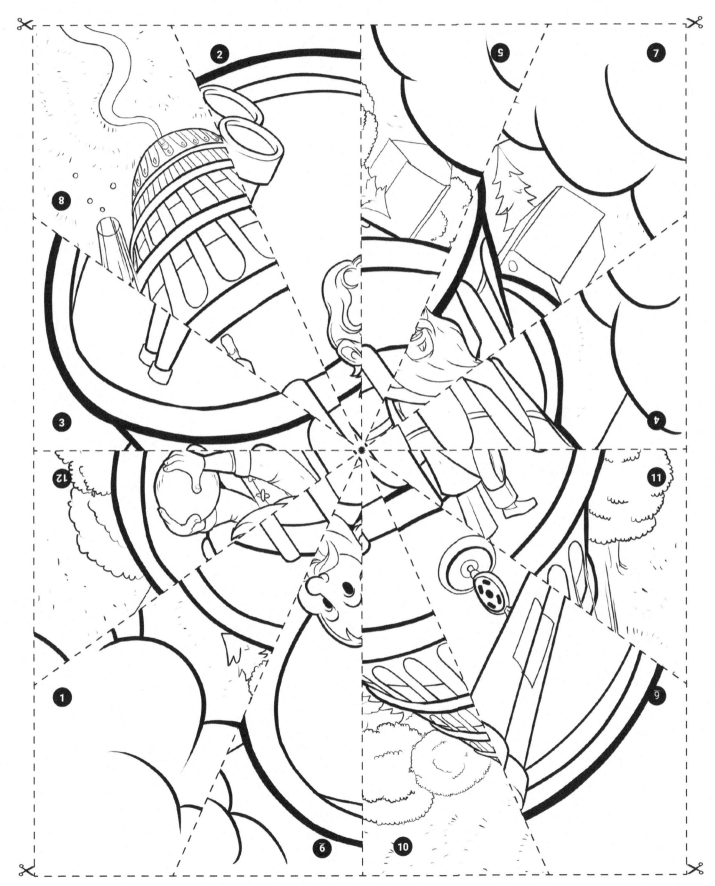

Galileo Galilei did an experiment. He climbed to the top of the Tower of Pisa. He dropped 2 cannon balls that were different weights. The balls hit the ground at the exact same time.

Solution on page 159

42÷7= __

14÷7= __

63÷7= __

49÷7= __

21÷7= __

84÷7= __

28÷7= __

77÷7= __

7÷7= __

56÷7= __

35÷7= __

70÷7= __

✏️ **I have a problem!** Today, we printed our weekly newspaper. We will deliver the papers for the next 7 days throughout our town. We printed 84 newspapers. How many will be delivered each day? Write the division problem and solve. Draw your answer if you want.

_____ ÷ _____ = _____

Sun

Mon

Tues

Wed

Thurs

Fri

Sat

The Wright Brothers

Solution on page 159

Help Marie classify her experiments. Count the bubbles and write the number in the box. Next, cut out the equations at the bottom of the page and glue each one on to the correct beaker with the answer.

Example - 7÷7= 1 bubble

Solution on page 159

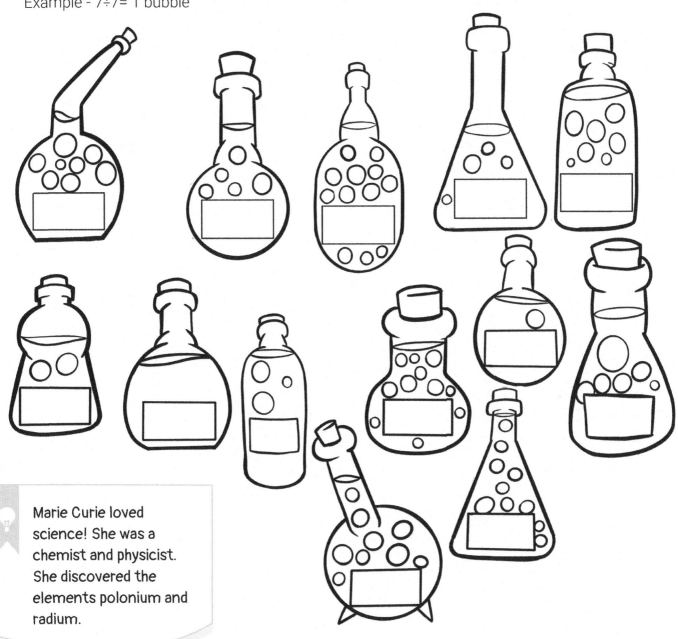

Marie Curie loved science! She was a chemist and physicist. She discovered the elements polonium and radium.

Marie Curie

14÷7	77÷7	28÷7
42÷7	21÷7	56÷7
70÷7	49÷7	84÷7
63÷7	7÷7	35÷7

Write the answer to each division problem on the puzzle frame. Color, cut, and glue the puzzle pieces to the frame with the matching answers to complete the puzzle.

Alexander Graham Bell is credited with inventing the telephone in 1876. Early phones had cables.

Solution on page 159

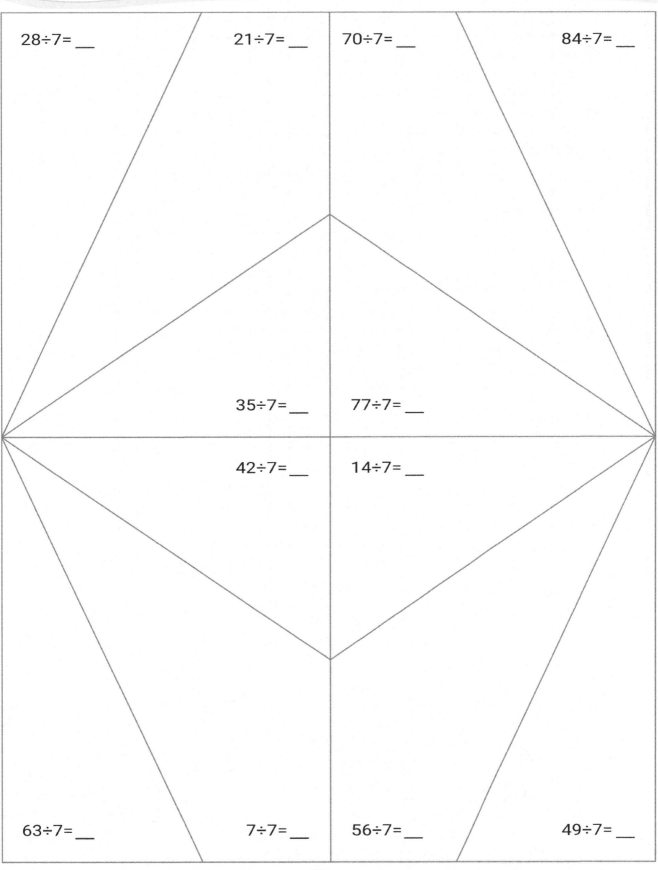

28÷7= __

21÷7= __

70÷7= __

84÷7= __

35÷7= __

77÷7= __

42÷7= __

14÷7= __

63÷7= __

7÷7= __

56÷7= __

49÷7= __

Solve the division problems. Then, color each pixel with the correct color to reveal the image.

$56 \div 7 =$
Light skin color

$21 \div 7 =$
Yellow

$84 \div 7 =$
White

$49 \div 7 =$
Light green

$63 \div 7 =$
Dark pink

$77 \div 7 =$
Gray

$14 \div 7 =$
Purple

$28 \div 7 =$
Orange

$42 \div 7 =$
Blue

$7 \div 7 =$
Violet

$70 \div 7 =$
Black

$35 \div 7 =$
Red

Solution on page 159

This is Nikola Tesla. He is best known for his work with electricity. He found a way to produce electric energy that could travel long distances.

Complete the dot-to-dot by finding the quotients. Start with the division problem that has an answer of 1.

$84 \div 7$ $70 \div 7$ $77 \div 7$ $56 \div 7$ $49 \div 7$ $63 \div 7$ $42 \div 7$ $28 \div 7$ $14 \div 7$ $35 \div 7$ $21 \div 7$ $7 \div 7$

Grade the Megageex
George Washington Carver took a math test! Grade his answers carefully! ✗ or ✓

Solution on page 159

Part 1: Each correct answer earns George Washington Carver 8 points.

○ $56 \div 7 = 8$ ○ $84 \div 7 = 12$ ○ $63 \div 7 = 4$

○ $35 \div 7 = 5$ ○ $42 \div 7 = 6$ ○ $49 \div 7 = 7$

○ $7 \div 7 = 1$ ○ $21 \div 7 = 4$

○ $28 \div 7 = 4$ ○ $14 \div 7 = 2$

Part 2: Challenge Problems! Each correct answer earns George Washington Carver 5 points each.

○ $77 \div 7 = 11$ ○ $28 \div 4 = 8$

   ○ $70 \div 7 = 10$ ○ $42 \div 6 = 7$

Calculate George Washington Carver's final grade!

Part 1 [ ] **X 8** = [ ]
CORRECT ANSWERS   POINTS PER ANSWER

My grade is _____

Part 2 [ ] **X 5** = [ ]
CORRECT ANSWERS   POINTS PER ANSWER

Part 1 [ ] + **Part 2** [ ] = [ ]
POINTS   POINTS   GRADE

George Washington Carver

Matching Game. Match the division problem on the left side of the page to its answer on the right side.

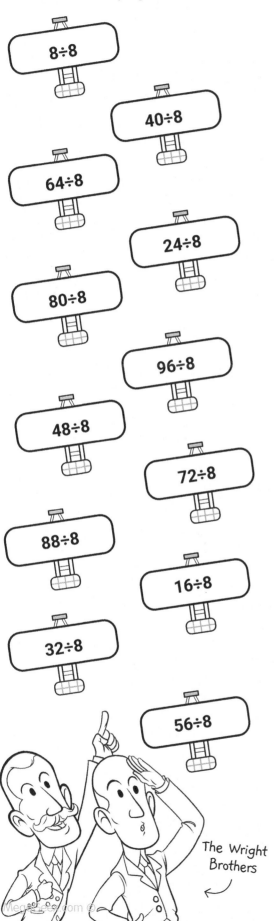

8÷8

40÷8

64÷8

24÷8

80÷8

96÷8

48÷8

72÷8

88÷8

16÷8

32÷8

56÷8

The Wright Brothers

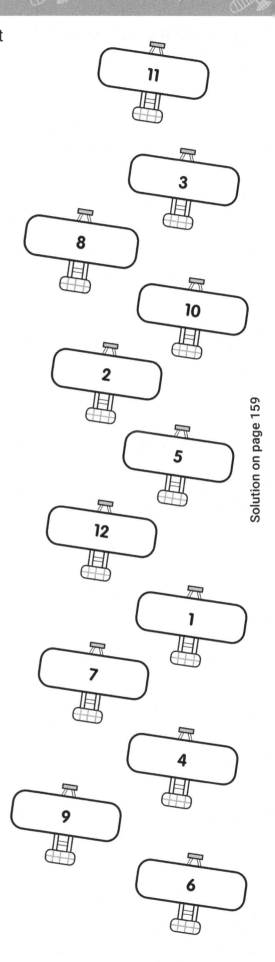

11

3

8

10

2

5

12

1

7

4

9

6

Solution on page 159

84

✏️ Draw a line through the correct path of the maze by solving the division problems. The answer to the problem will show you the way and reveal the hidden item!

Solution on page 159

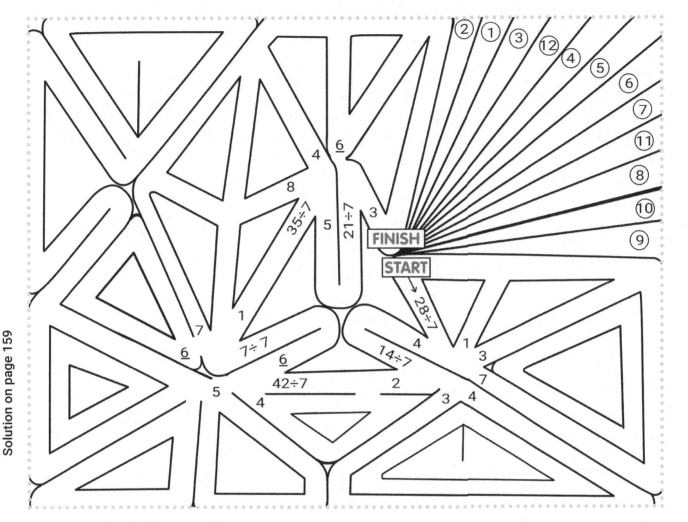

What's the hidden item? _____

✏️ Complete the division problems in the color key. Find the circled numbers in the maze and color the picture using the color indicated.

What shape did you get? ◹ ◭ ▽ ◿

63÷7= Red	56÷7= Dark blue	7÷7= Orange
28÷7= Purple	42÷7= Yellow	70÷7= Green
49÷7= Pink	21÷7= Light blue	14÷7= Blue
77÷7= Brown	84÷7= Light green	35÷7= Light Red

Isaac Newton

Isaac Newton noticed that water and glass create rainbows. He then used prisms to show that light is made up of seven colors. Newton used the prism to study the science of how we see things.

MegaGeex.com ©

An umbrella kept the sun from tanning women's faces. Jane believed that following your dreams was more important than appearances.

Complete the division problems in the color key to discover the colors to use in the picture.

56÷8= Red	40÷8= Light green	24÷8= Blue	80÷8= Light brown	16÷8= Light blue	48÷8= Dark green
8÷8= Light skin color	64÷8= Yellow	88÷8= Orange	32÷8= Gray	96÷8= Purple	72÷8= White

Solution on page 160

What's wrong? Look at each problem carefully.
Circle only the problems that are correct.

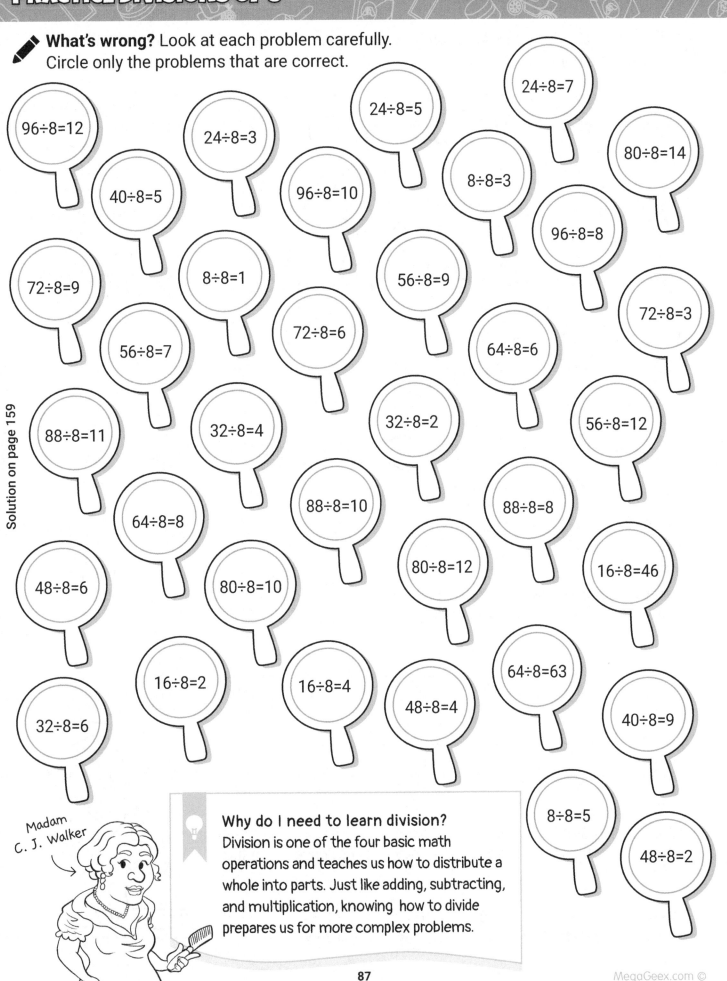

96÷8=12

40÷8=5

24÷8=3

24÷8=5

24÷8=7

80÷8=14

96÷8=10

8÷8=3

96÷8=8

72÷8=9

8÷8=1

56÷8=9

72÷8=3

56÷8=7

72÷8=6

64÷8=6

88÷8=11

32÷8=4

32÷8=2

56÷8=12

64÷8=8

88÷8=10

88÷8=8

48÷8=6

80÷8=10

80÷8=12

16÷8=46

16÷8=2

16÷8=4

64÷8=63

32÷8=6

48÷8=4

40÷8=9

8÷8=5

48÷8=2

Solution on page 159

Madam
C. J. Walker

Why do I need to learn division?
Division is one of the four basic math
operations and teaches us how to distribute a
whole into parts. Just like adding, subtracting,
and multiplication, knowing how to divide
prepares us for more complex problems.

✏️ Complete the dot-to-dot by finding the quotients. Start with the division problem that has an answer of 1.

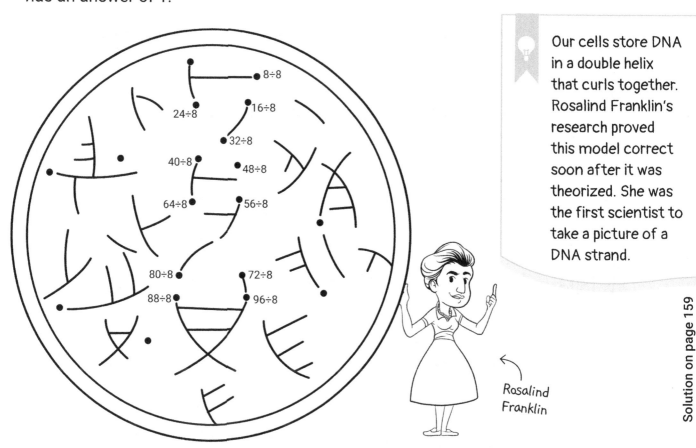

Our cells store DNA in a double helix that curls together. Rosalind Franklin's research proved this model correct soon after it was theorized. She was the first scientist to take a picture of a DNA strand.

Rosalind Franklin

Solution on page 159

✏️ Find the answers to each division problem. Write the word(s) on the lines with the matching answers to see the message.

___ ___ ___ ___ ___ ___
1   12   3   8   2   9

___ ___ ___ ___ ___ ___
7   6   11   5   10   4

| 40÷8= be | 48÷8= should | 56÷8= and | 64÷8= day | 8÷8= Science | 16÷8= life |

| 72÷8= cannot | 80÷8= separated | 88÷8= not | 96÷8= and | 24÷8= every | 32÷8= ! |

Who Stole My Number? In the equations below, there is a number missing!
Fill in the missing numbers!

Solution on page 159

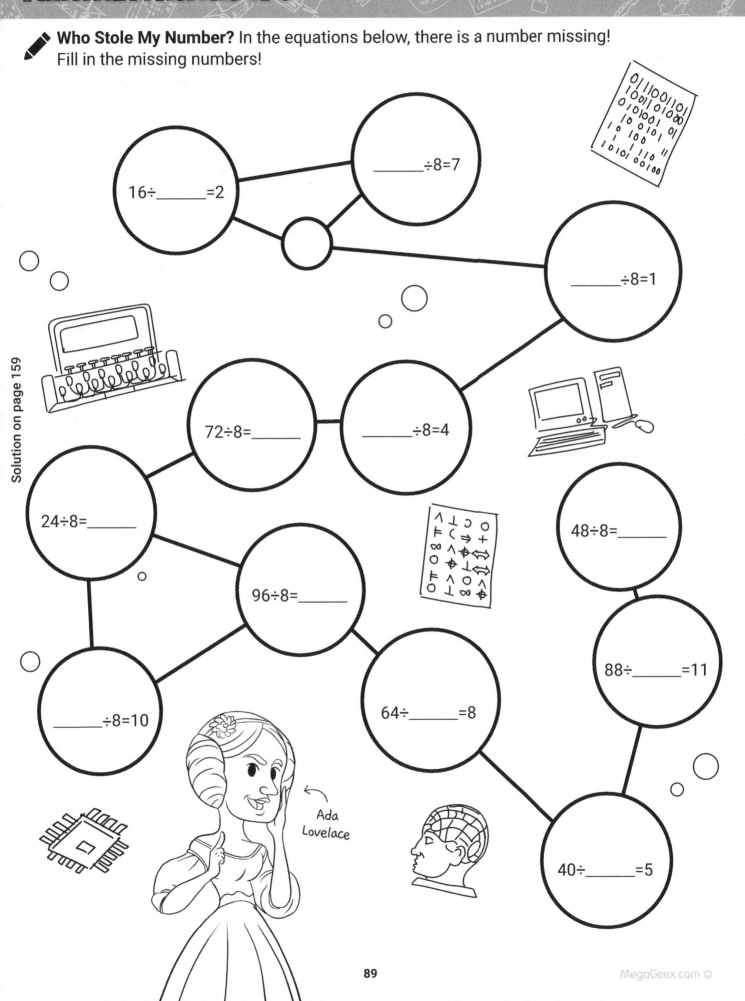

$16÷$_____$=2$

_____$÷8=7$

_____$÷8=1$

$72÷8=$_____

_____$÷8=4$

$24÷8=$_____

$48÷8=$_____

$96÷8=$_____

_____$÷8=10$

$64÷$_____$=8$

$88÷$_____$=11$

$40÷$_____$=5$

Ada Lovelace

MegaGeex.com ©

✏ **I have a problem!** My invention of the telephone made it possible for people to talk to each other when they were far apart. People were excited to have telephones in their homes. In one neighborhood, there were 16 phones and 8 houses. How many phones were in each house?

Write the division problem and solve. Draw a picture showing your answer if you want.

_____ ÷ _____ = _____

Alexander Graham Bell

Solution on page 160

Grade the Megageex
Darwin took a math test! Grade his answers carefully! ✗ or ✓

Part 1: Each correct answer earns Charles 7 points.

64÷8= 8   24÷8= 3   80÷8= 10

96÷8= 12   48÷8= 8   32÷8= 4

72÷8= 7   56÷8= 7   88÷8= 11

40÷8= 5   8÷8= 1   16÷8= 2

Part 2: Challenge Problems! Each correct answer earns Charles 4 points each

14÷2= 6   21÷3= 7

18÷6= 2   60÷12= 5

Solution on page 160

Calculate Darwin's final grade!

Part 1 [ ] X **7** = [ ]
CORRECT   POINTS PER
ANSWERS   ANSWER

My grade is

_____

Part 2 [ ] X **4** = [ ]
CORRECT   POINTS PER
ANSWERS   ANSWER

Part 1 [ ] + **Part 2** [ ] = [ ]
POINTS   POINTS   GRADE

Charles
Darwin

Solve the division problems. Then, color each pixel with the correct color to reveal the image.

63÷9= Orange	18÷9= Yellow	81÷9= White	36÷9= Black	27÷9= Light green	108÷9= Pink
9÷9= Purple	99÷9= Dark blue	45÷9= Light blue	90÷9= Green	72÷9= Dark gray	54÷9= Light red

108÷9

99÷9   90÷9

72÷9   81÷9   9÷9

63÷9   54÷9

36÷9   45÷9

27÷9   18÷9

Thomas Edison

Solution on page 160

MegaGeex.com ©

92

✏ **Matching Game** Match the division problem on the left side of the page to its answer on the right side.

Solution on page 160

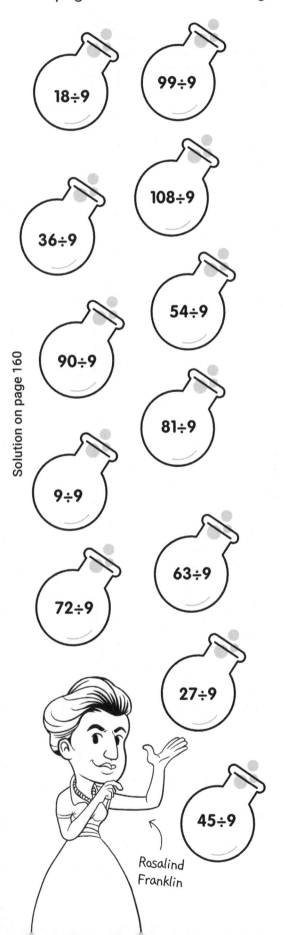

18÷9

99÷9

36÷9

108÷9

90÷9

54÷9

9÷9

81÷9

72÷9

63÷9

27÷9

45÷9

Rosalind
Franklin

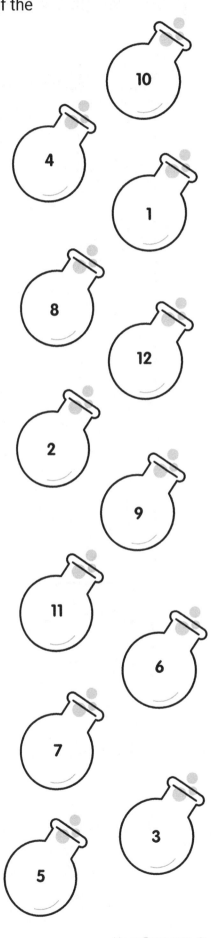

10

4

1

8

12

2

9

11

6

7

5

3

✏️ Complete the division problems in the color key to discover the colors to use in the picture.

Solution on page 160

9÷9= Orange	45÷9= Red	81÷9= Light red	18÷9= Light pink
27÷9= Green	63÷9= Purple	99÷9= Dark green	36÷9= Blue
54÷9= Yellow	90÷9= Light blue	72÷9= Pink	108÷9= Brown

Ada Lovelace wanted to study the brain using mathematics. Her goal was to discover how thoughts led to emotions that people feel.

Ada Lovelace

✏️ **What's wrong?** Look at each problem carefully.
Circle only the problems that are correct.

Solution on page 160

90÷9=10

9÷9=1

108÷9=10

99÷9=10

27÷9=3

36÷9=6

18÷9=4

81÷9=9

72÷9=8

18÷9=2

45÷9=7

99÷9=11

27÷9=2

54÷9=9

108÷9=13

54÷9=6

9÷9=0

36÷9=4

63÷9=7

90÷9=11

45÷9=5

81÷9=10

63÷9=5

72÷9=4

108÷9=12

54÷9=3

36÷9=8

27÷9=1

9÷9=3

90÷9=12

63÷9=3

18÷9=5

81÷9=8

99÷9=13

72÷9=6

45÷9=3

Jane
Austin

MegaGeex.com ©

Find the correct path through the Enigma maze. Solve the division problems along the way.

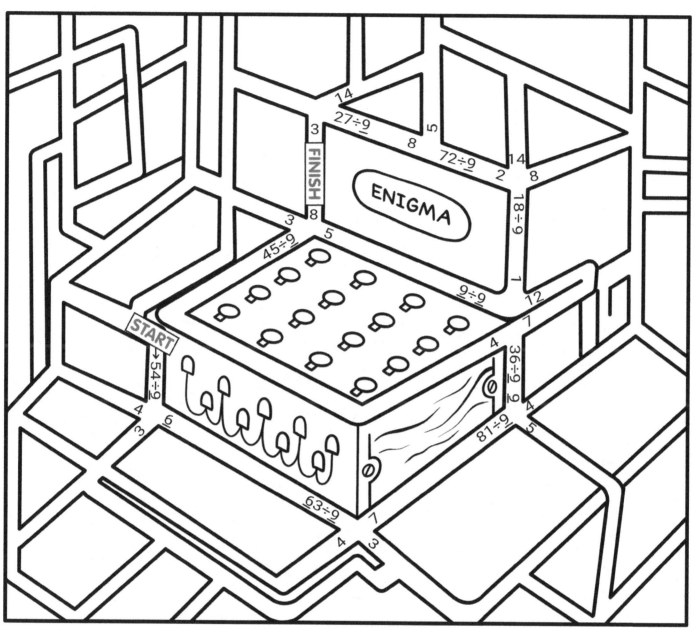

What's the hidden item? _____

Alan Turing

During World War II, Alan Turing designed a powerful code breaking machine called Enigma. This machine deciphered messages the Germans used and it helped the Allies defeat them.

✏️ Write the answer to each division problem on the puzzle frame. Color, cut, and glue the puzzle pieces to the frame with the matching answers to complete the puzzle.

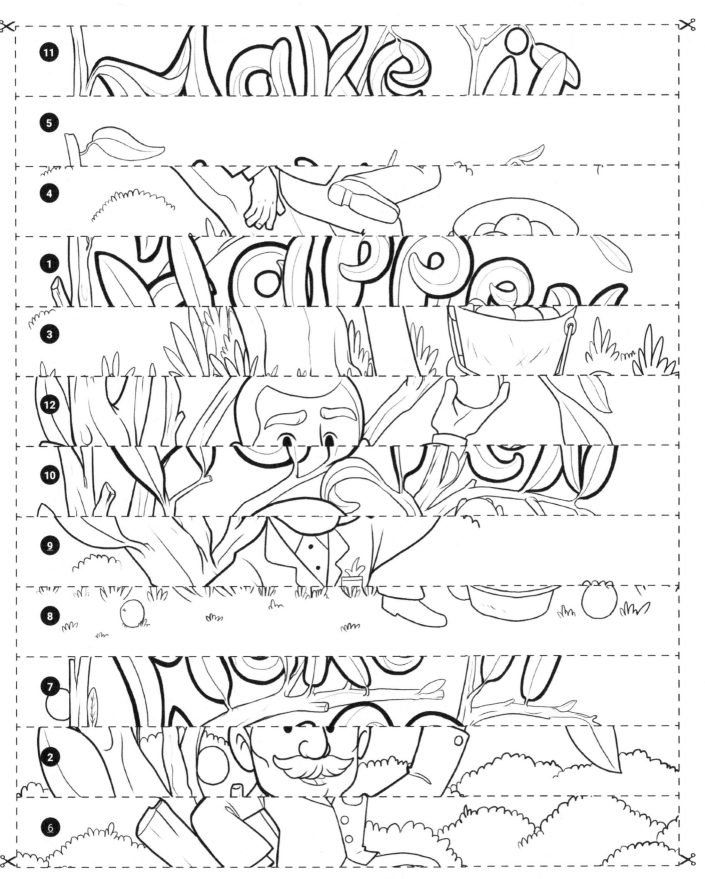

11

5

4

1

3

12

10

9

8

7

2

6

George Washington Carver overcame many challenges as a Black man in the 1800s in America. He became a successful agricultural scientist and inventor.

Solution on page 160

$99 \div 9 = \underline{\ \ }$

$45 \div 9 = \underline{\ \ }$

$63 \div 9 = \underline{\ \ }$

$9 \div 9 = \underline{\ \ }$

$90 \div 9 = \underline{\ \ }$

$108 \div 9 = \underline{\ \ }$

$18 \div 9 = \underline{\ \ }$

$81 \div 9 = \underline{\ \ }$

$54 \div 9 = \underline{\ \ }$

$36 \div 9 = \underline{\ \ }$

$27 \div 9 = \underline{\ \ }$

$72 \div 9 = \underline{\ \ }$

Who Stole My Number? In the equations below, there is a number missing! Fill in the missing numbers!

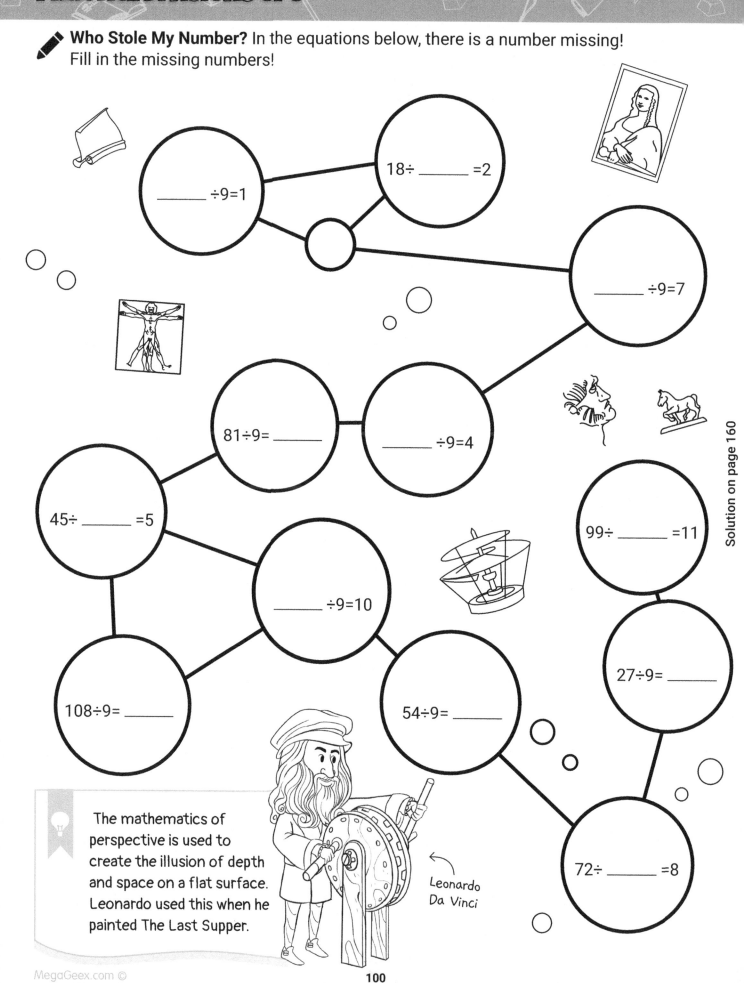

_____ ÷9=1

18÷ _____ =2

_____ ÷9=7

81÷9= _____

_____ ÷9=4

45÷ _____ =5

99÷ _____ =11

_____ ÷9=10

108÷9= _____

54÷9= _____

27÷9= _____

72÷ _____ =8

Leonardo Da Vinci

The mathematics of perspective is used to create the illusion of depth and space on a flat surface. Leonardo used this when he painted The Last Supper.

Solution on page 160

I have a problem! When I was only 8 years old, my father, sister and I traveled all over Europe performing for royalty. We once performed 18 times in 9 nine days. How many performances did we complete each day?

Write the division problem and solve. Draw a picture showing your answer if you want.

Solution on page 160

_____ ÷ _____ = _____

Day 1

Day 2

Day 3

Day 4

Day 5

Day 6

Day 7

Day 8

Day 9

Wolfgang Amadeus Mozart

Grade the Megageex
Marie Curie took a math test! Grade her answers carefully! or

Part 1: Each correct answer earns Marie 8 points.

◯ 54÷9= 6   ◯ 45÷9= 6   ◯ 81÷9= 9

◯ 90÷9= 10   ◯ 108÷9= 12   ◯ 18÷9= 2

◯ 27÷9= 2   ◯ 63÷9= 7   ◯ 99÷9= 11

◯ 72÷9= 8   ◯ 36÷9= 4   ◯ 9÷9= 1

Part 2: Challenge Problems! Each correct answer earns Marie 1 point each.

◯ 80÷8 = 10   ◯ 48÷6= 8

◯ 14÷2= 7   ◯ 32÷4= 8

Solution on page 160

Calculate Marie's final grade!

Part 1 [___] X **8** = [___]
CORRECT ANSWERS   POINTS PER ANSWER

Part 2 [___] X **1** = [___]
CORRECT ANSWERS   POINTS PER ANSWER

Marie Curie →

My grade is
____

Part 1 [___] + **Part 2** [___] = [___]
POINTS   POINTS   GRADE

Complete the dot-to-dot by finding the quotients. Start with the division problem that has an answer of 1. Darwin's dot-to dot has two parts. Complete the left side first, then do the right.

20÷10   30÷10
10÷10   60÷10 70÷10
100÷10 110÷10
40÷10 50÷10
90÷10   80÷10

20÷10   30÷10
10÷10   60÷10 70÷10
100÷10 110÷10
40÷10 50÷10
90÷10   80÷10

Charles Darwin

The last recording sighting of a Dodo bird was in 1662. Scientists wondered why the bird went extinct. Charles Darwin believed in survival of the fittest, but no one knows why the bird disappeared.

PRACTICE DIVISIONS OF 10

✏️ **Matching Game.** Match the division problem on the left side of the page to its answer on the right side.

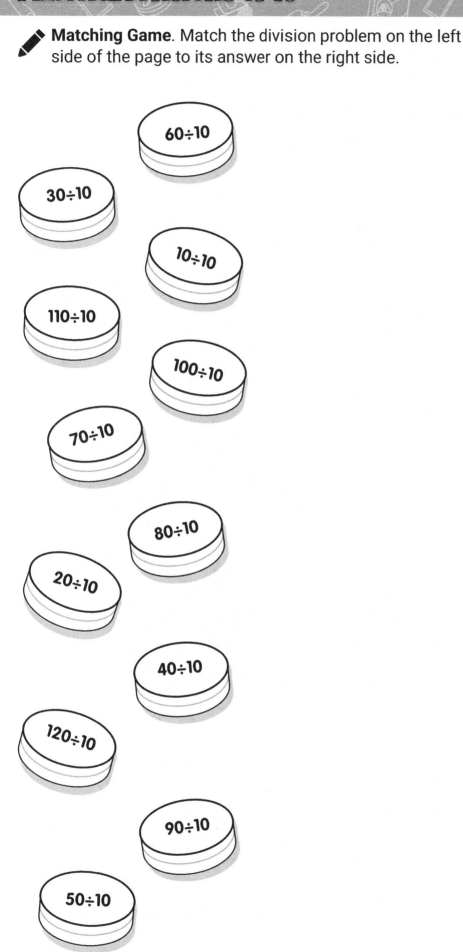

60÷10

30÷10

10÷10

110÷10

100÷10

70÷10

80÷10

20÷10

40÷10

120÷10

90÷10

50÷10

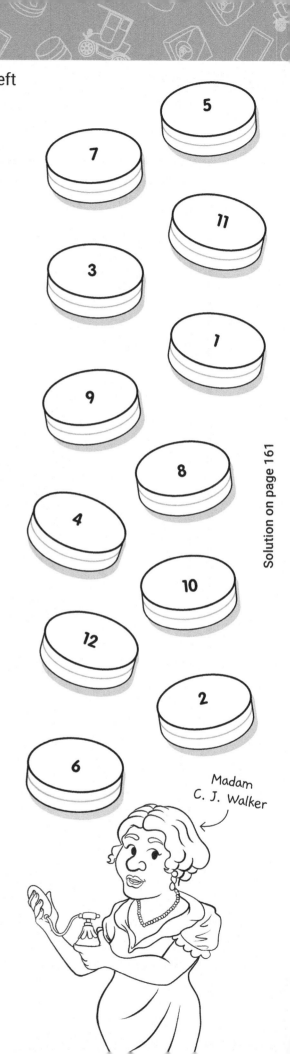

5

7

11

3

1

9

8

4

10

12

2

6

Madam C. J. Walker

Solution on page 161

Draw a line through the correct path of the maze by solving the division problems. The answer to the problem will show you the way and reveal the hidden item!

Solution on page 161

Mozart's career focused mainly on keyboard instruments, but he started playing the violin when he was five years old.

What's the hidden item? _____

Wolfgang Amadeus Mozart

MegaGeex.com ©

✏ **What's wrong?** Look at each problem carefully. Circle only the problems that are correct.

100÷10=10

10÷10=3

50÷10=3

20÷10=2

80÷10=6

10÷10=2

70÷10=5

20÷10=1

20÷10=3

40÷10=4

30÷10=3

80÷10=4

90÷10=9

120÷10=11

40÷10=1

50÷10=5

60÷10=4

120÷10=10

90÷10=7

10÷10=1

70÷10=3

50÷10=10

110÷10=11

30÷10=7

100÷10=12

30÷10=5

90÷10=3

60÷10=6

Alan
Turing

120÷10=12

70÷10=7

60÷10=8

100÷10=11

40÷10=8

110÷10=10

110÷10=12

80÷10=8

Solution on page 161

MegaGeek.com

106

Complete the division problems in the color key to discover the colors to use in the picture.

70÷10=	50÷10=	30÷10=	120÷10=	20÷10=	40÷10=
Brown	Yellow	Gray	Green	Light purple	Light skin color

10÷10=	110÷10=	90÷10=	60÷10=	80÷10=	100÷10=
Purple	Light green	Dark red	Light blue	Pink	Blue

Who Stole My Number? In the equations below, there is a number missing! Fill in the missing numbers!

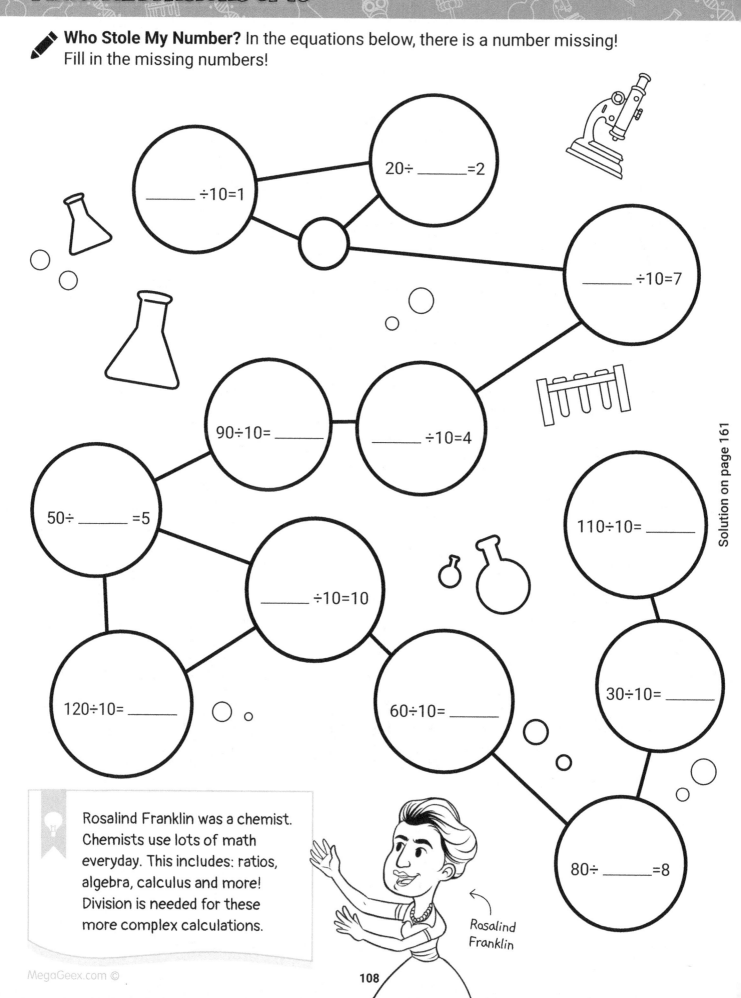

_____ ÷10=1

20÷_____=2

_____ ÷10=7

90÷10=_____

_____ ÷10=4

50÷_____=5

110÷10=_____

_____ ÷10=10

120÷10=_____

60÷10=_____

30÷10=_____

80÷_____=8

Solution on page 161

Rosalind Franklin was a chemist. Chemists use lots of math everyday. This includes: ratios, algebra, calculus and more! Division is needed for these more complex calculations.

Rosalind Franklin

108

Complete the division problems in the color key to discover the colors to use in the picture.

 With Galileo's improved telescope, he became the first person to see the rings of Saturn and 4 of Jupiter's inner moons.

Solution on page 161

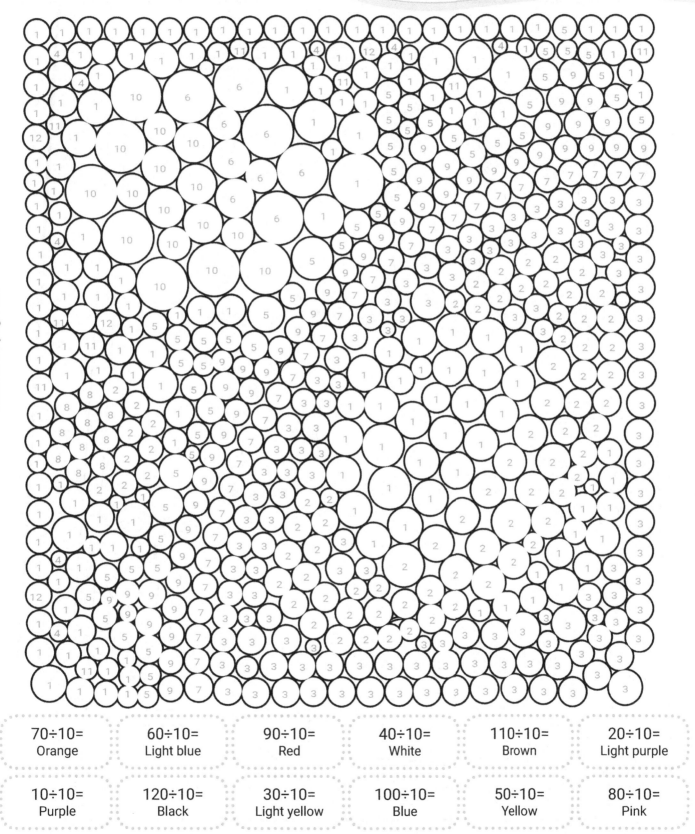

70÷10= Orange	60÷10= Light blue	90÷10= Red	40÷10= White	110÷10= Brown	20÷10= Light purple
10÷10= Purple	120÷10= Black	30÷10= Light yellow	100÷10= Blue	50÷10= Yellow	80÷10= Pink

MegaGeex.com ©

✏ **I have a problem!** The night I was born, there was a severe lightning storm! In one hour there were 60 lighting strikes. How many lightning strikes were there every 10 minutes? Write the division problem and solve. Draw a picture showing your answer if you want.

_____ ÷ _____ = _____

Solution on page 161

Nikola Tesla

✎ **Grade the Megageex**
Amadeus Mozart took a math test! Grade his answers carefully! ✗ or ✓

Solution on page 161

Part 1: Each correct answer earns Wolfgang 3 points.

○ 50÷10= 5   ○ 10÷10= 1   ○ 90÷10= 9

○ 120÷10= 12   ○ 60÷10= 9   ○ 100÷10= 10

○ 40÷10= 4   ○ 20÷10= 2   ○ 30÷10= 3

○ 110÷10= 11   ○ 80÷10= 8   ○ 70÷10= 7

Part 2: Challenge Problems! Each correct answer earns Mozart 8 points.

○ 49÷7 = 6   ○ 35÷5= 6   ○ 36÷3= 12   ○ 16÷4= 4

○ 54÷6= 9   ○ 24÷8= 3   ○ 36÷6= 6   ○ 16÷8= 3

Calculate Mozart's final grade!

Part 1 [____] X **3** = [____]
CORRECT ANSWERS   POINTS PER ANSWER

Part 2 [____] X **8** = [____]
CORRECT ANSWERS   POINTS PER ANSWER

My grade is
_____

Part 1 [____] + **Part 2** [____] = [____]
POINTS   POINTS   GRADE

Wolfgang
Amadeus
Mozart

✎ **I have a problem!** My favorite food is baked apple dumplings. I have 121 apples. Each pan of apple dumplings requires 11 apples. How many pans of dumplings can I bake? Write the division problem and solve. Draw a picture showing your answer if you want.

_____ ÷ _____ = _____

Thomas Edison

Solution on page 161

✏️ **Matching Game.** Match the division problem on the left side of the page to its answer on the right side.

Solution on page 161

11÷11

44÷11

88÷11

110÷11

132÷11

22÷11

66÷11

99÷11

33÷11

121÷11

55÷11

77÷11

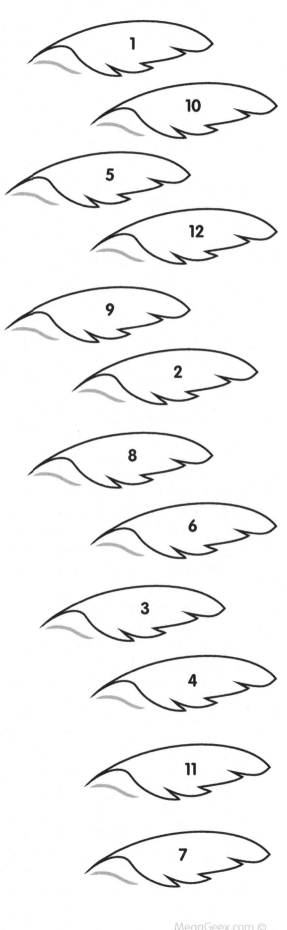

1

10

5

12

9

2

8

6

3

4

11

7

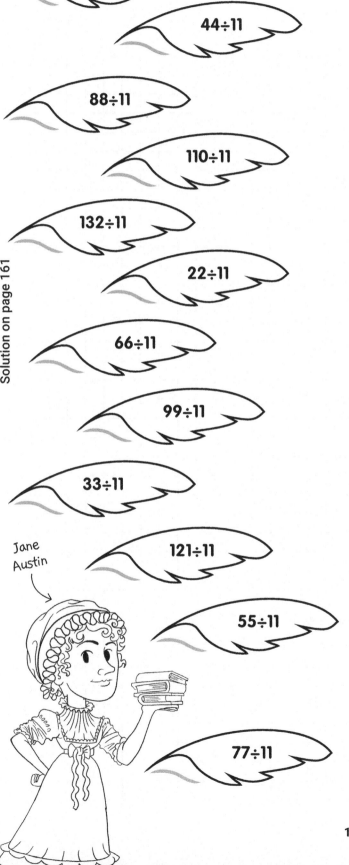

Jane
Austin

113

Solve the division problems. Then, color each pixel the correct color to reveal the image.

77÷11= Purple	22÷11= Dark pink	66÷11= Light purple
44÷11= Green	121÷11= Yellow	33÷11= Orange
11÷11= Pink	88÷11= Blue	99÷11= Dark blue
110÷11= Red	55÷11= Light blue	132÷11= White

Rosalind Franklin used her research with coal to take the famous first picture of a DNA strand. The picture was called Photo 51.

Solution on page 161

What's wrong? Look at each problem carefully.
Circle only the problems that are correct.

Solution on page 162

132÷11=12
99÷11=9
66÷11=6
110÷11=12
44÷11=4
132÷11=11
11÷11=1
77÷11=7
55÷11=5
22÷11=4
88÷11=6
33÷11=7
44÷11=6
99÷11=8
121÷11=10
110÷11=10
11÷11=0
88÷11=8
121÷11=12
33÷11=5
88÷11=9
66÷11=5
22÷11=6
33÷11=3
44÷11=8
77÷11=8
77÷11=6
55÷11=7
11÷11=3
99÷11=7
55÷11=3
22÷11=2
66÷11=4
132÷11=14
110÷11=11
121÷11=11
132÷11=14

Leonardo
Da Vinci

115

MegaGeex.com ©

✏️ Complete the dot-to-dot by finding the quotients. Start with the division problem that has an answer of 1.

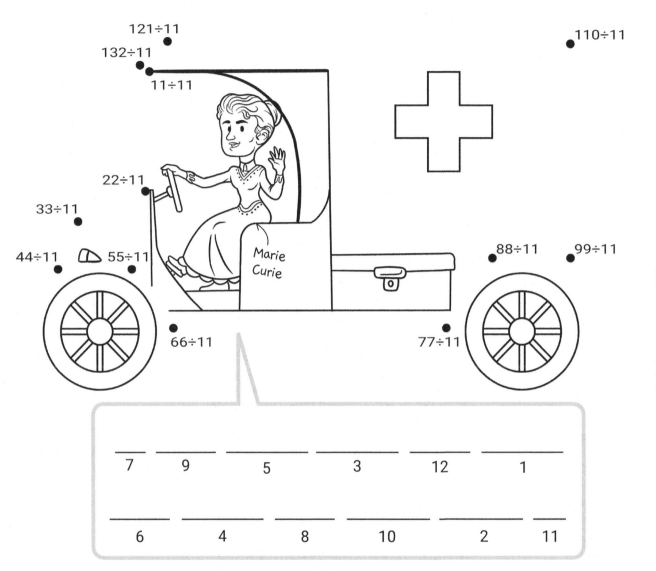

121÷11
132÷11
11÷11
110÷11
22÷11
33÷11
44÷11 55÷11
88÷11 99÷11
66÷11 77÷11

Marie Curie

Solution on page 162

7	9	5	3	12	1
6	4	8	10	2	11

✏️ Find the answers to each division problem. Write the words on the lines with the matching answers to see the message.

99÷11= am	66÷11= that	33÷11= those	132÷11= who
88÷11= has	22÷11= beauty	77÷11= I	55÷11= among
11÷11= think	110÷11= great	121÷11= ♡	44÷11= science

In World War I, Marie Curie devised a plan to make X-ray machines portable so that more injured soldiers could be treated in field hospitals. The machines were transported in vehicles called "Little Curies."

Who Stole My Number? In the equations below, there is a number missing! Fill in the missing numbers!

Solution on page 162

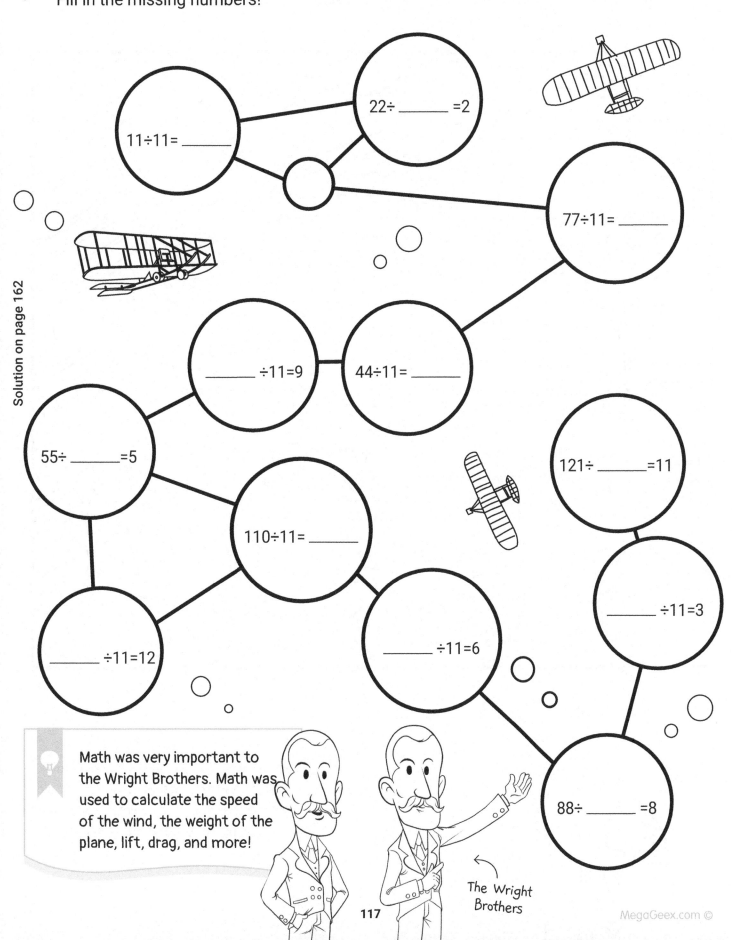

$11 \div 11 =$ _____

$22 \div$ _____ $= 2$

$77 \div 11 =$ _____

_____ $\div 11 = 9$

$44 \div 11 =$ _____

$55 \div$ _____ $= 5$

$110 \div 11 =$ _____

$121 \div$ _____ $= 11$

_____ $\div 11 = 3$

_____ $\div 11 = 12$

_____ $\div 11 = 6$

$88 \div$ _____ $= 8$

Math was very important to the Wright Brothers. Math was used to calculate the speed of the wind, the weight of the plane, lift, drag, and more!

The Wright Brothers

117

MegaGeex.com ©

PRACTICE DIVISIONS OF 11

✒ Draw a line through the correct path of the maze by solving the division problems. The answer to the problem will show you the way and reveal the hidden item!

Solution on page 162

What's the hidden item? _____

Nikola Tesla

> As early as 1892, Tesla designed a radio. It was soon after he discovered he could transmit and receive powerful radio signals. His filed his first radio patent in 1897.

MegaGeex.com®

118

✏️ Write the answer to each division problem on the puzzle frame. Color, cut, and glue the puzzle pieces to the frame with the matching answers to complete the puzzle.

PRACTICE DIVISIONS OF 11

33÷11= __	77÷11= __	66÷11= __
110÷11= __	55÷11= __	99÷11= __
44÷11= __	88÷11= __	22÷11= __
11÷11= __	132÷11= __	121÷11= __

Solution on page 162

✏ Grade the Megageex

Rosalind Franklin took a math test! Grade her answers carefully! ✗ or ✓

Part 1: Each correct answer earns Rosalind 7 points.

○ 77÷11= 7   ○ 44÷11= 4   ○ 33÷11= 3

○ 121÷11= 11   ○ 66÷11= 6   ○ 110÷11= 10

○ 55÷11= 5   ○ 11÷11= 1   ○ 22÷11= 2

○ 99÷11= 9   ○ 88÷11= 8   ○ 132÷11= 13

Part 2: Challenge Problems! Each correct answer earns Rosalind 4 points each.

○ 96÷8 = 7   ○ 50÷5= 10

       ○ 72÷9= 7   ○ 48÷8= 6

Calculate Franklin's final grade!

Part 1 [   ] X **7** = [   ]

CORRECT   POINTS PER
ANSWERS   ANSWER

My grade is

_____

Part 2 [   ] X **4** = [   ]

CORRECT   POINTS PER
ANSWERS   ANSWER

Part 1 [   ] **+** **Part 2** [   ] **=** [   ]

POINTS   POINTS   GRADE

Rosalind
Franklin

Solution on page 162

Complete the division problems in the color key to discover the colors to use in the picture.

Solution on page 162

A gear is a machine usually shaped in a circle with "teeth." Gears work together to make more power in a machine. Leonardo da Vinci was the first to study gear wheels and the process of gearing.

Leonardo Da Vinci

96÷12= Light pink	24÷12= Green	132÷12= Light brown	48÷12= Yellow
60÷12= Purple	108÷12= Blue	84÷12= Pink	72÷12= Orange
12÷12= Red	120÷12= Light blue	36÷12= Brown	144÷12= Gray

MegaGeex.com ©

PRACTICE DIVISIONS OF 12

✏️ **Matching Game**. Match the division problem on the left side of the page to its answer on the right side.

12÷12

84÷12

132÷12

24÷12

96÷12

60÷12

36÷12

120÷12

144÷12

48÷12

72÷12

108÷12

Charles Darwin

12

7

4

9

1

2

5

8

3

10

6

11

Solution on page 162

Complete the dot-to-dot by finding the quotients. Start with the division problem that has an answer of 1. Color, cut, and glue the puzzle pieces to the frame with the matching answers to complete the puzzle answers to complete the puzzle.

Solution on page 162

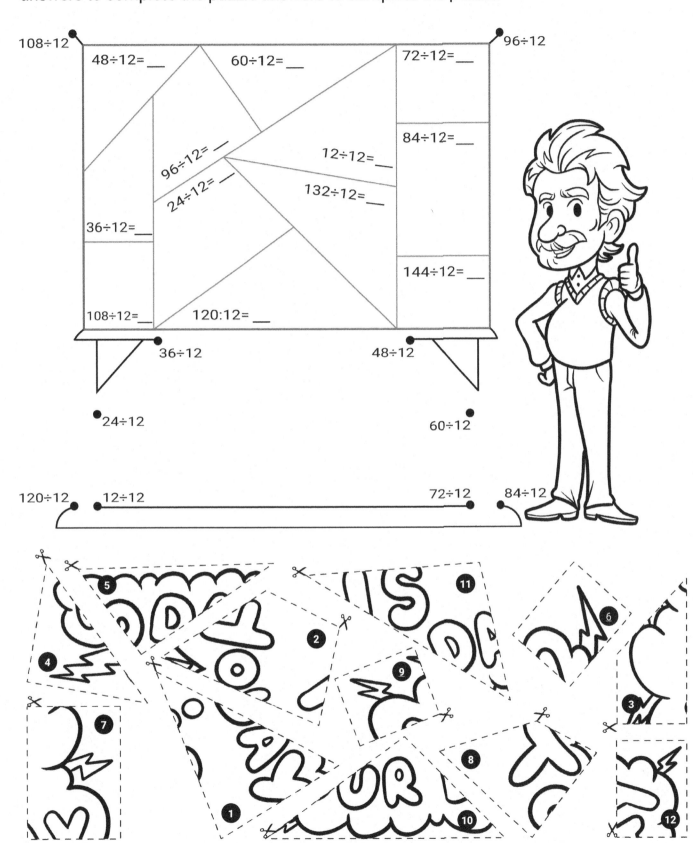

108÷12   96÷12

48÷12=__   60÷12=__   72÷12=__

96÷12=__   84÷12=__

24÷12=__   12÷12=__

132÷12=__

36÷12=__

144÷12=__

108÷12=__   120:12=__

36÷12   48÷12

24÷12   60÷12

120÷12   12÷12   72÷12   84÷12

✏ **What's wrong?** Look at each problem carefully.
Circle only the problems that are correct.

Solution on page 162

12÷12=1

132÷12=11

96÷12=10

24÷12=6

60÷12=9

120÷12=11

84÷12=7

108÷12=9

72÷12=6

48÷12=2

144÷12=12

84÷12=11

36÷12=3

144÷12=11

12÷12=2

120÷12=12

24÷12=4

132÷12=12

48÷12=4

72÷12=8

60÷12=7

84÷12=9

96÷12=6

72÷12=4

132÷12=10

96÷12=8

36÷12=5

108÷12=7

48÷12=6

12÷12=3

24÷12=2

60÷12=5

120÷12=10

36÷12=7

144÷12=10

108÷12=5

Isaac
Newton

127

Complete the division problem in the color key to discover the colors to use in the picture.

Solution on page 162

84÷12= Gray	24÷12= Blue	72÷12= Dark gray	120÷12= Purple	60÷12= Purple	36÷12= Brown
12÷12= Light blue	108÷12= Pink	96÷12= Lilac	48÷12= Orange	132÷12= Light green	144÷12= Green

 Galileo loved exploring the solar system with his telescope. Previous telescopes could magnify objects three times. Galileo worked until his telescope could magnify objects ten times.

✏ **Who Stole My Number?** In the equations below, there is a number missing! Fill in the missing numbers!

Solution on page 162

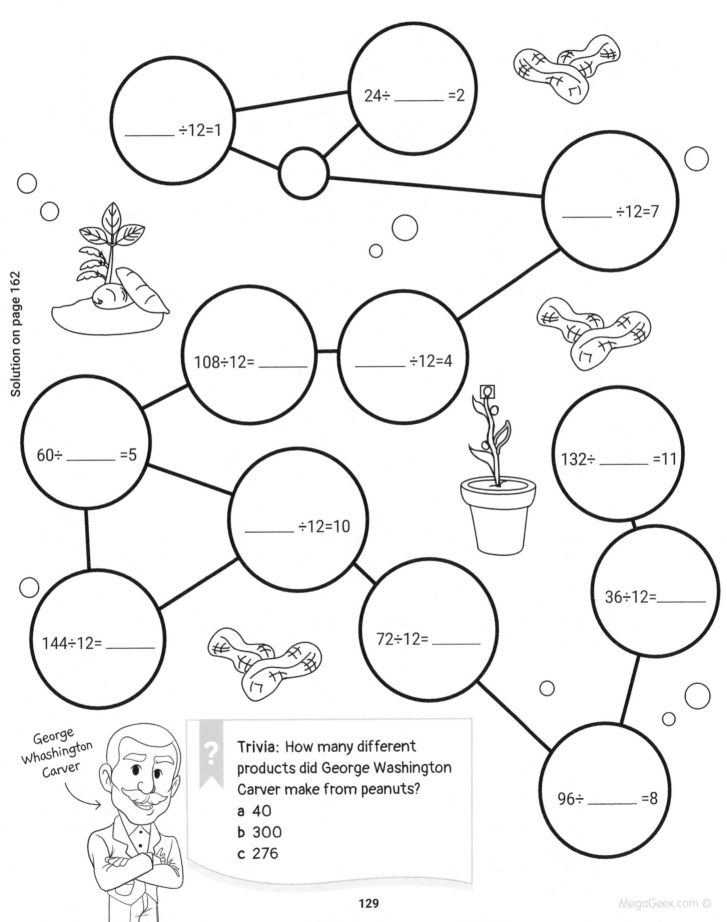

_____ ÷12=1

24÷ _____ =2

_____ ÷12=7

108÷12= _____

_____ ÷12=4

60÷ _____ =5

132÷ _____ =11

_____ ÷12=10

36÷12= _____

144÷12= _____

72÷12= _____

96÷ _____ =8

George Whashington Carver

Trivia: How many different products did George Washington Carver make from peanuts?
a 40
b 300
c 276

Draw a line through the correct path of the maze by solving the division problems. The answer to the problem will show you the way and reveal the hidden item!

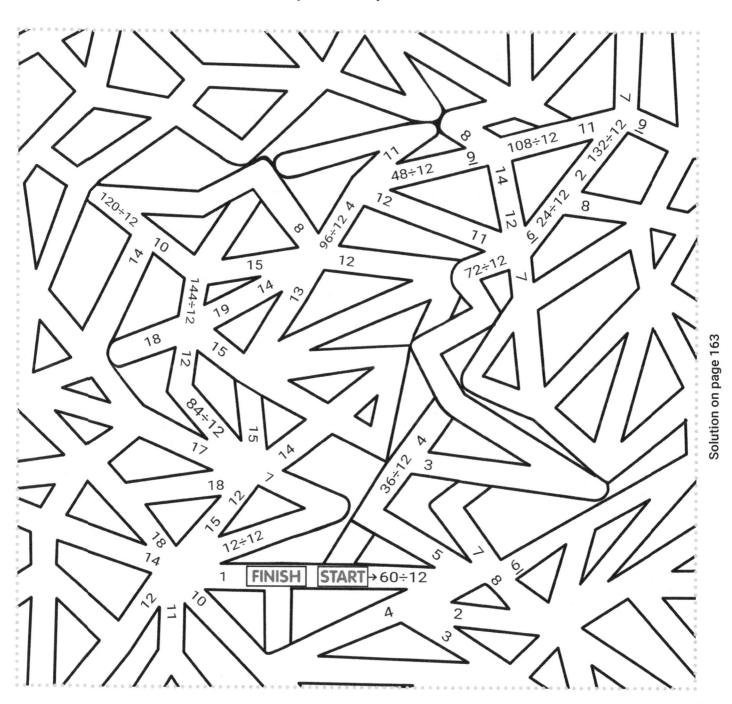

Solution on page 163

What's the hidden item? _____

Ada Lovelace

Ada Lovelace became ill with the measles as a child. While confined to her bed, she studied birds and thought of a plan to make a flying machine.

MegaGeex.com ©

130

✎ **I have a problem!** In my life, we did not have television or radios. For fun we liked to play card games. One game we played, there were 72 cards in the deck. There are 12 players in this game? How many cards does each player get?
Write the division problem and solve. Draw a picture showing your answer if you want.

Solution on page 163

_____ ÷ _____ = _____

Isaac Newton

Grade the Megageex

Alexander Graham Bell took a math test! Grade his answers carefully! or

Part 1: Each correct answer earns Alexander 5 points.

◯ 96÷12= 8   ◯ 132÷12= 11   ◯ 24÷12= 2

◯ 48÷12= 4   ◯ 72÷12= 6   ◯ 120÷12= 10

◯ 36÷12= 3   ◯ 144÷12= 12   ◯ 84÷12= 7

◯ 108÷12= 9   ◯ 12÷12= 1   ◯ 60÷12= 5

Part 2: Challenge Problems! Each correct answer earns Alexander 8 points each.

◯ 22÷11 = 2   ◯ 88÷10= 10   ◯ 72÷9= 9

◯ 132÷11= 12   ◯ 12÷2= 5

Solution on page 163

Calculate Bell's final grade!

Part 1 [　] X **5** = [　]

CORRECT ANSWERS   POINTS PER ANSWER

My grade is

_____

Part 2 [　] X **8** = [　]

CORRECT ANSWERS   POINTS PER ANSWER

Part 1 [　] + Part 2 [　] = [　]

POINTS   POINTS   GRADE

Alexander Graham Bell

✏️ Write the answer to each division problem on the puzzle frame. Color, cut, and glue the puzzle pieces to the frame with the matching answers to complete the puzzle.

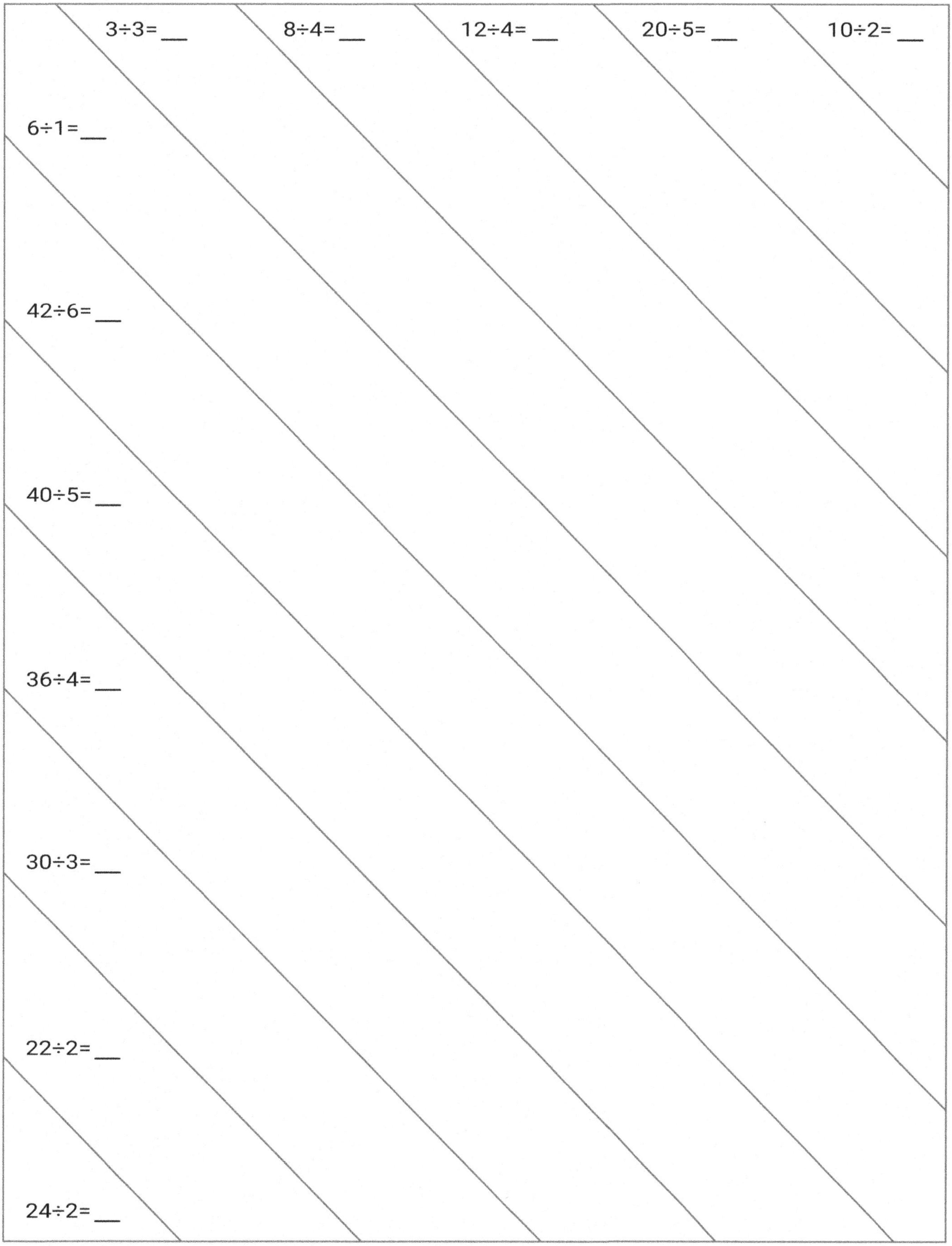

3÷3= __

8÷4= __

12÷4= __

20÷5= __

10÷2= __

6÷1= __

42÷6= __

40÷5= __

36÷4= __

30÷3= __

22÷2= __

24÷2= __

Solution on page 163

✏️ Write the answer to each division problem on the puzzle frame. Color, cut, and glue the puzzle pieces to the frame with the matching answers to complete the puzzle.

George Washington Carver

Nikola Tesla

Wolfgang Amadeus Mozart

Charles Darwin

Madam C.J. Walker

MegaGeex.com ©

Solution on page 163

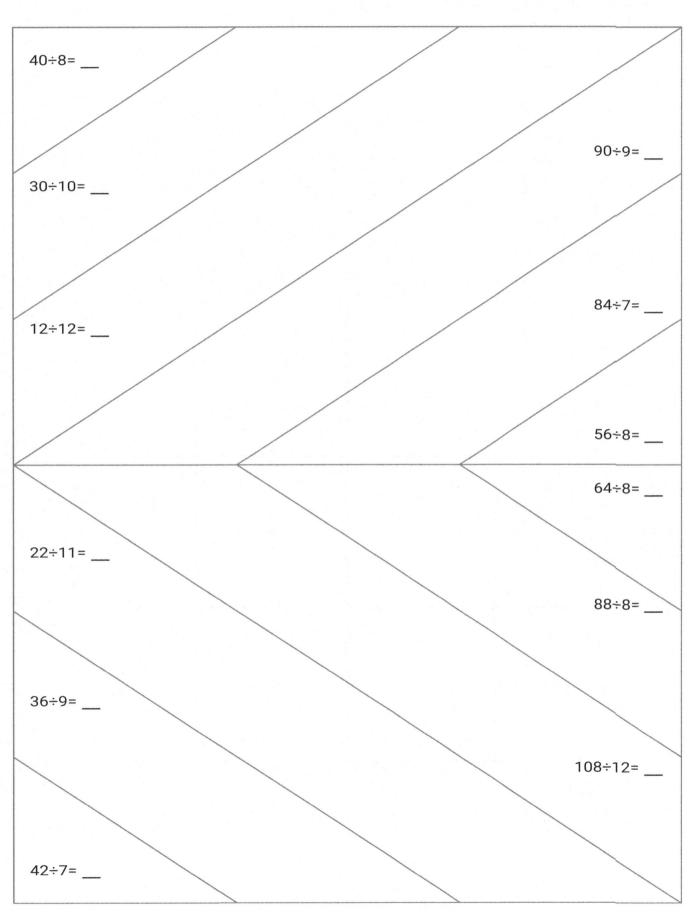

40÷8= __

30÷10= __

12÷12= __

90÷9= __

84÷7= __

56÷8= __

64÷8= __

22÷11= __

88÷8= __

36÷9= __

108÷12= __

42÷7= __

SUDOKU

Complete the division problems and fill in the missing numbers so all numbers 1 to 6 appear once in every row, column and grid.

Solution on page 163

4÷4= ___	8÷4= ___	9÷3= ___	12÷3= ___	36÷6= ___	20÷4= ___
16÷4= ___	25÷5= ___		6÷6= ___	6÷3= ___	
24÷4= ___		5÷5= ___	15÷5= ___	30÷6= ___	4÷2= ___
12÷6= ___	6÷2= ___	15÷3= ___	30÷5= ___		8÷2= ___
18÷6= ___	3÷3= ___	10÷5= ___	10÷2= ___	4÷1= ___	12÷2= ___
	18÷3= ___	20÷5= ___		12÷4= ___	2÷2= ___

SUDOKU

Complete the division problems and fill in the missing numbers so all numbers 7 to 12 appear once in every row, column and grid.

Solution on page 163

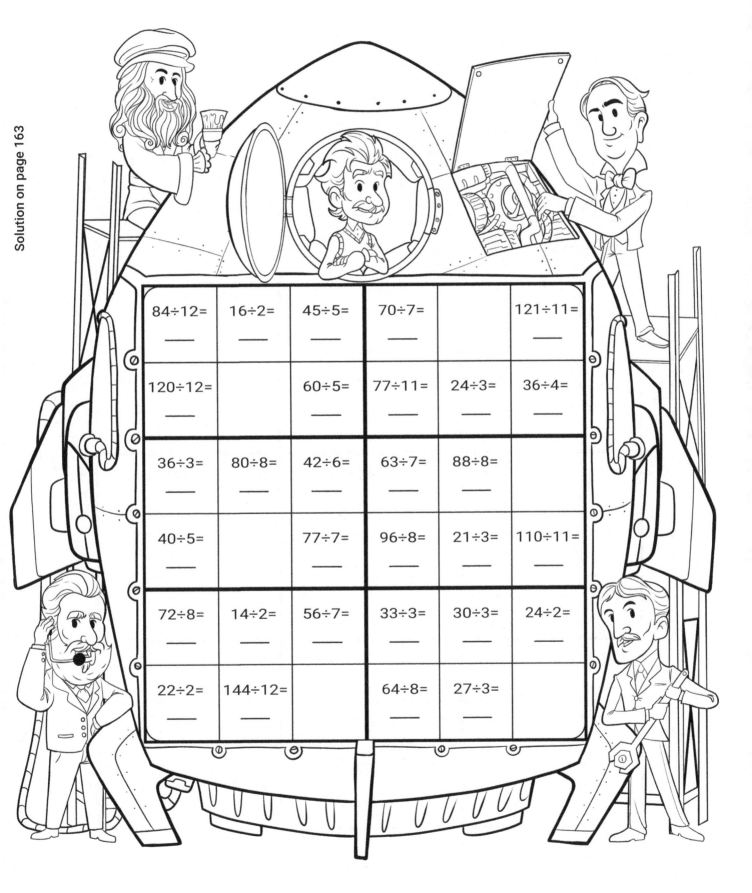

84÷12= ___	16÷2= ___	45÷5= ___	70÷7= ___		121÷11= ___
120÷12= ___		60÷5= ___	77÷11= ___	24÷3= ___	36÷4= ___
36÷3= ___	80÷8= ___	42÷6= ___	63÷7= ___	88÷8= ___	
40÷5= ___		77÷7= ___	96÷8= ___	21÷3= ___	110÷11= ___
72÷8= ___	14÷2= ___	56÷7= ___	33÷3= ___	30÷3= ___	24÷2= ___
22÷2= ___	144÷12= ___		64÷8= ___	27÷3= ___	

SUDOKU

Complete the division problems and fill in the missing numbers so all numbers 1 to 9 appear once in every row, column and grid.

33÷11=	8÷4=	14÷2=	6÷6=	25÷5=	48÷6=	18÷2=	36÷9=	
	10÷10=	45÷5=	24÷6=	12÷4=	35÷5=	55÷11=	8÷1=	22÷11=
60÷12=	28÷7=	16÷2=		24÷4=	12÷6=	28÷4=	7÷7=	9÷3=
	88÷11=	66÷11=	50÷10=	63÷9=	40÷10=	6÷2=	4÷2=	27÷3=
16÷4=	21÷9=	10÷5=	30÷5=	40÷5=	54÷6=	12÷12=	20÷4=	21÷3=
36÷4=	49÷7=	35÷7=	18÷6=		9÷9=	12÷3=	12÷2=	
56÷8=	36÷6=	48÷12=	14÷7=		30÷10=	32÷4=	108÷12=	45÷9=
72÷9=		8÷8=	42÷6=	81÷9=	48÷8=	2÷1=	15÷5=	
18÷9=	63÷7=	24÷8=	96÷12=	20÷5=	40÷8=	72÷12=	84÷12=	4÷4=

Solution on page 163

DIVISION TOWER

Now that you are a division master, the Megageex need your help! It's getting cold, and each window in the tower needs to be covered. Match the window pieces to each correct answer.

Albert Einstein

HOW TO BUILD THE TOWER

1

Color the tower. Then, carefully cut out the two tower wall pieces and the roof section.

2

Assemble the tower by matching and gluing the tabs as indicated.

3

Cut out each window piece on the dotted lines. Then, fold them on the dotted line.

4

Above each Megageex is the answer to a problem. Cover the Megageex characters on the tower with the window pieces displaying the correct division problem.

35	÷7	18	÷3	20	÷5	12	÷6
33	÷3	25	÷5	24	÷2	24	÷3
10	÷11	9	÷3	8	÷2	5	÷5
40	÷12	36	÷6	20	÷2	21	÷3

60	÷9

÷3	24		18	5		÷5	÷5		21	÷6
33	÷3		25	÷5		÷7	÷2		12	÷7
÷6	36		9	21		÷3	20		÷8	20
21	8		÷7	24		÷2	÷2		÷3	35

| 88 | ÷3 |

16: **Matching Game**

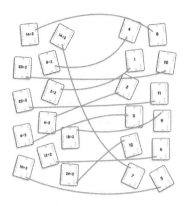

17: **Newton's Apple**

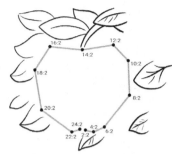

Secret Message: "If I have seen further than others, it is by standing upon the shoulders of giants"

18: Who stole my number?

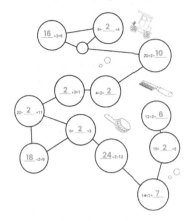

19: **The Mona Lisa**

20: **What's wrong?**

21: **Gas Mask**

22: **I have a problem**

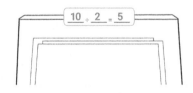

23: Ada Lovelace **Puzzle**

25: **Grade the Megageex**

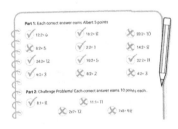

26: **What's wrong?**

27: **The Wright Flyer**

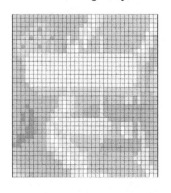

28: **I have a problem**

29: **Edison's Light Bulb**

30: **Matching Game**

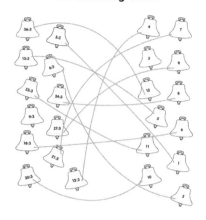

31: **Darwin and Fossils**

Triceratops

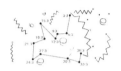

32: **Who stole my number?**

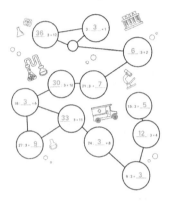

33: **Grade the Megageex**

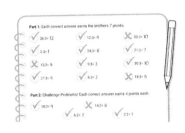

34: **Tesla Coil**

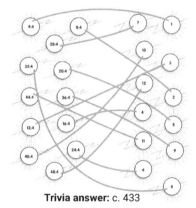

37: **Who stole my number?**

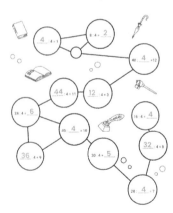

38: **Jupiter and Saturn**

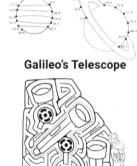

Galileo's Telescope

39: **Matching Game**

Trivia answer: c. 433

40: **What's wrong?**

43: Wolfgang Amadeus Mozart **Puzzle**

44: Madam C.J. Walker **Color by number**

45: **I have a problem**

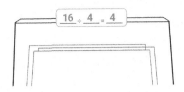

$$16 \div 4 = 4$$

46: **Alan Turing's First Computer**

47: **Grade the Megageex**

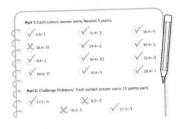

48: **Matching Game**

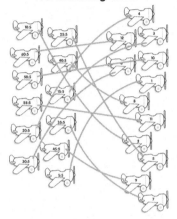

49: **Bell's Hydrofoil**

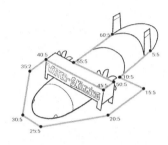

Secret Message: "The achievement of one objective should be the starting point of anoter"

50: **What's wrong?**

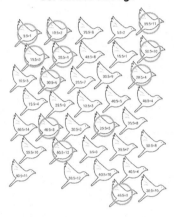

51: George Washington Carver **Maze**

51: **I have a problem**

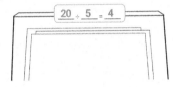

$$20 \div 5 = 4$$

53: **Albert Einstein Connect the dots**

55: **Who stole my number?**

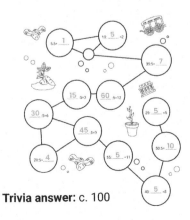

Trivia answer: c. 100

56: Marie Curie **Pixel**

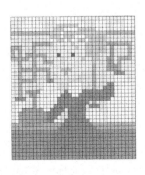

57: **Grade the Megageex**

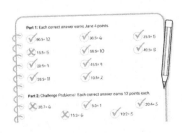

58: Matching Game

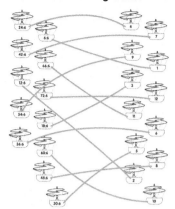

59: Quill Pen

Color by number

60: What's wrong?

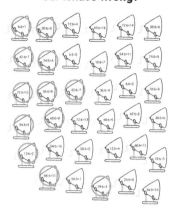

61: Darwin's Pick Axe

62: Who stole my number?

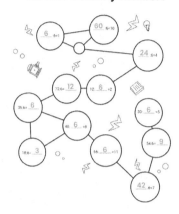

65: The Wright Brothers Puzzle

66: I have a problem

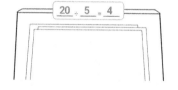

67: Madam C.J. Walker Color by number

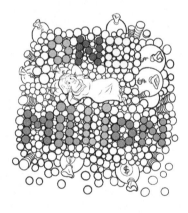

68: Grade the Megageex

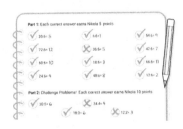

69: Matching Game

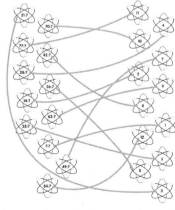

70: Leonardo Da Vinci Maze

Items in maze: Parachute, Glider, Gears, Aerial Screw, Mona Lisa, Horse Model, Brain Sketch, Paddle Boat, Bicycle, Catapult, Scroll

71: What's wrong?

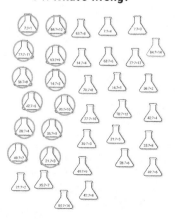

72: Who stole my number?

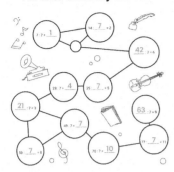

Trivia answer: c. 24 zeros:
1,000,000,000,000,000,000,000,000

75: Galileo Galilei Puzzle

76: I have a problem

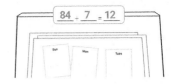

77: Marie Curie

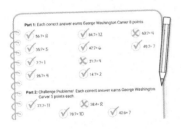

81: Alexander Graham Bell Puzzle

82: Nikola Tesla Pixel

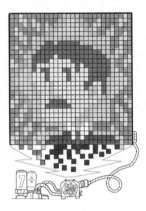

83: Grade the Megageex

84: Matching Game

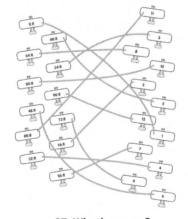

85: Color Prism

"The shape is: △ "

86: Edisons Dynamo Electric Machine

87: What's wrong?

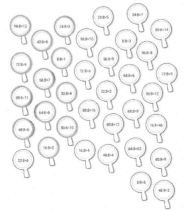

88: DNA Double Helix

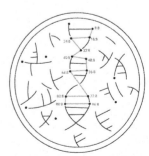

Secret Message: "Science and everyday life cannot and should not be separated."

89: Who stole my number?

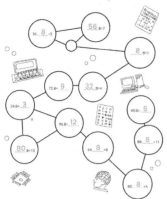

90: I have a problem

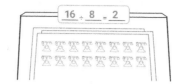

$$16 \div 8 = 2$$

91: Grade the Megageex

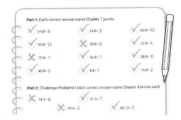

92: Edison's Dynamo Electric Machine

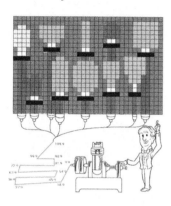

93: Matching Game

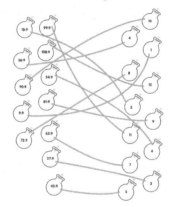

94: Ada Lovelace and the Human Brain

95: What's wrong?

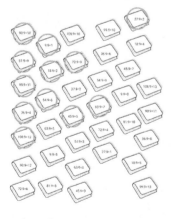

96: Alan Turing Maze

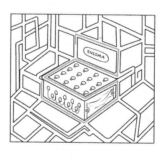

99: George Washington Carver Puzzle

100: Who stole my number?

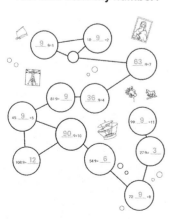

101: I have a problem

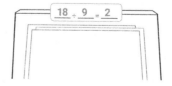

$$18 \div 9 = 2$$

102: Grade the Megageex

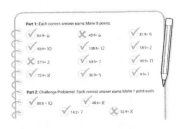

103: The Dodo Bird

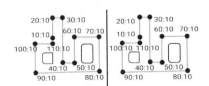

104: Matching Game

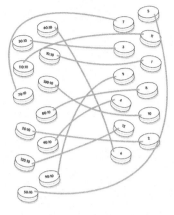

105: Violin

106: What's wrong?

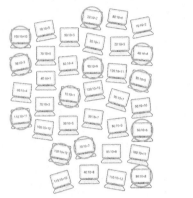

107: Albert Einstein Color by number

108: Who stole my number?

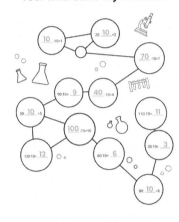

109: Saturn, Jupiter and Jupiter's Moons

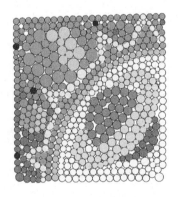

110: I have a problem

60 ÷ 10 = 6

111: Grade the Megageex

112: I have a problem

121 ÷ 11 = 22

113: Matching Game

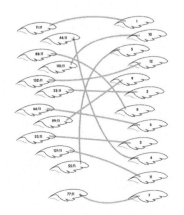

114: DNA Double Helix Structure

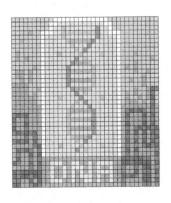

MegaGeex.com ©

SOLUTIONS

115: What's wrong?

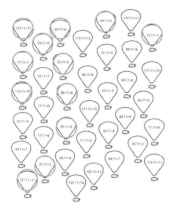

116: Portable X-ray Units-Little Curies

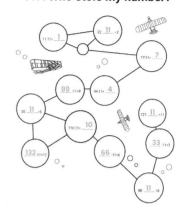

Secret Message: "I am among those who think that science has great beauty"

117: Who stole my number?

118: Radio

121: Galileo's Telescope

122: Grade the Megageex

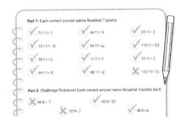

123: Leonardo Da Vinci Color by number

124: Matching Game

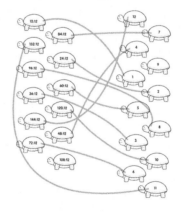

125: Albert Einstein Puzzle

127: What's wrong?

128: Galileo Galilei Color by number

129: Who stole my number?

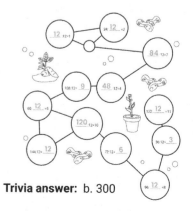

Trivia answer: b. 300

130: Bird

131: I have a problem

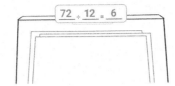

$$72 \div 12 = 6$$

132: Grade the Megageex

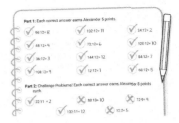

Part 1: Each correct answer earns Alexander 5 points.

✓ 96:12=8	✓ 132:12=11	✓ 34:12=10
✓ 48:12=4	✓ 72:12=6	✓ 120:12=10
✓ 36:12=3	✓ 144:12=12	✓ 84:12=7
✓ 108:12=9	✓ 12:12=1	✓ 66:12=5

Part 2: Challenge Problems! Each correct answer earns Alexander 8 points each.

✓ 22:11=2	✗ 88:10=10	✗ 72:9=9
✓ 132:11=12		✗ 12:2=5

135: Puzzle

139: Puzzle

140: Sudoku

4:4=1	8:4=2	9:3=3	12:3=4	36:6=6	20:4=5
16:4=4	25:5=5	6	6:6=1	6:3=2	3
24:4=6	4	5:5=1	15:5=3	30:5=6	4:2=2
12:6=2	6:2=3	15:3=5	30:5=6	1	8:2=4
18:6=3	3:3=1	10:5=2	10:2=5	4:1=4	12:2=6
5	18:3=6	20:5=4	2	12:4=3	2:2=1

141: Sudoku

84:12=7	16:2=8	45:5=9	70:7=10	12	121:11=11
120:12=10	11	60:5=12	77:11=7	24:3=8	36:4=9
36:3=12	80:8=10	42:6=7	63:7=9	88:8=11	8
40:5=8	9	77:7=11	96:8=12	21:3=7	110:11=10
72:8=9	14:2=7	56:7=8	33:3=11	30:3=10	24:2=12
22:2=11	144:12=12	10	64:8=8	27:3=9	7

142: Sudoku

33:11=3	8:4=2	14:2=7	6:6=1	25:5=5	48:6=8	18:2=9	36:9=4	6
6	10:10=1	45:5=9	24:6=4	12:4=3	35:5=7	55:11=5	8:1=8	22:11=7
60:12=5	28:7=4	16:2=8	9	24:4=6	12:6=2	28:4=7	7:7=1	9:3=3
1	88:11=8	66:11=6	50:10=5	63:9=7	40:10=4	6:2=3	4:2=2	27:3=9
16:4=4	21:9=3	10:5=2	30:5=6	40:5=8	54:6=9	12:12=1	20:4=5	21:3=7
36:4=9	49:7=7	35:7=5	18:6=3	2	9:9=1	12:3=4	12:2=6	8
56:8=7	36:6=6	48:12=4	14:7=2	1	30:10=3	32:4=8	108:12=9	45:9=5
72:9=8	5	8:8=1	42:6=7	81:9=9	48:8=6	2:1=2	15:5=3	4
18:9=2	63:7=9	24:8=3	96:12=8	20:5=4	40:8=5	72:12=6	84:12=7	4:4=1

Finished the book?
Well done!

Send us a video and receive a
certificate diploma from Megageex!
support@megageex.com

How can you get more
out of MegaGeex?

Subscribe to our newsletter at
www.MegaGeex.com and follow us on
Instagram and Facebook
to receive free activity pages to inspire
your kids.

🌐   www.MegaGeex.com

📷   MegaGeex

📘   MegaGeexCom

Take learning to a whole new level and bring the Megageex to life with these 3D DIY Books

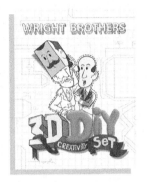  

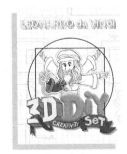   

"Beautiful details. My son loved building it and playing with all the elements included."

★ ★ ★ ★ ★

Linda N, USA.